GROWING HERBS WITH MARGARET ROBERTS

Growing Herbs
with Margaret Roberts

A guide to growing herbs in South Africa

Illustrated by Joan van Gogh

Southern Book Publishers

ISBN 1 86812 110 0

First Published in 1985 by
Jonathan Ball Publishers
Second impression 1986

First edition, first impression 1988
First edition, second impression 1990
First edition, third impression 1991

Published by
Southern Book Publishers (Pty) Limited
PO Box 3103
Halfway House
1685

Design and phototypesetting by Book Productions, Pretoria
Printed and bound by The Penrose Press, Johannesburg

To those who love gardening

CONTENTS

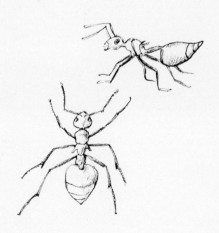

FOREWORD

Using herbs to cure herself of illness after years of suffering was a powerful reason for becoming enthusiastic about the medicinal properties of these gifts of nature, but Margaret Roberts is more than enthusiastic – she is dedicated to studying their histories and medicinal potential in order to help others.

Today, working with herbs – growing, experimenting and studying them – has become a way of life for Margaret and through her books she is sharing her knowledge with the many people who are excited by her work. Her first book, simply entitled *Margaret Roberts' Book of Herbs*, sold extremely well and this book, *Growing Herbs with Margaret Roberts*, is its companion volume. This must surely be proof of her ability and of the large and eager following of readers anxious to share her knowledge.

Several years ago, when interviewing her on behalf of a national magazine, Margaret told me that she first became interested in herbs when, as a young mother on a farm in the Magaliesberg, cut off from doctors, she found herself having to nurse a delicate, allergy-prone child for many years. Through courage and perseverance, and using nature's remedies, together they managed to overcome the allergies. It was not, however, until New Year's Day in 1978 that she finally made the decision to make herbs and the study of their medicinal value her life's work. 'Every New Year's Day I retire from the rest of the family, sit quietly and meditate on what I am going to do for the year,' she explained, 'and for 1978 my resolution was to concentrate on herbs. It turned out to be the most important decision of my life.'

It has not been an easy path to follow and there have been many battles and a great deal of trauma along the way. However, as with everything else Margaret does, she has come out on top.

Her father once gave her this advice: 'You need three things in life for success – persistence, determination and enthusiasm,' and to this Margaret has added one extra attribute – fight. She says herself, 'I have always had a breathing problem and this has made a fighter of me, for if you don't fight you die – and so I have learned to see things through. I must always tie up threads.' This she has certainly done with this fine new book.

She has garnered in this volume the essence of what she has learned over long years as a grower of herbs in adverse conditions of appalling heat, cold, frost, wind and drought. Included are carefully documented medicinal uses, methods of preparation and dosages, as well as the methods of growing 100 herbs. In a period of only four months she has, in her own words, 'unravelled the thread of the magic carpet of herbs'.

Margaret's ultimate aim, she once told me, was to take a plant and turn it into medicine and then see the results achieved by that medicine. In this book she is able to share with us much of what she has discovered along the road – and if the end is not yet in sight, for her, this is certainly an important milestone along the way and one which will delight all those interested in the fascinating lore of herbs.

Owen A Reid

ACKNOWLEDGEMENTS

I am privileged in the caring group of friends who surrounded me in the writing of this book, and I feel unable to thank them adequately for what they have done in getting me and the book together.

On a hot afternoon in February 1984 Jonathan Ball called me to his office and announced that we needed a companion to *Margaret Roberts' Book of Herbs*, and he gave me only a few months in which to complete it. This was probably the most positive thing that could have happened to me in a time of tremendous personal crisis and grief. It was a therapy to rise in the dawn and put pen to paper and think above the pain, to dig deeply around my beloved plants and turn up all the information I could. For that forced discipline and the chance he gave me, Jonathan Ball will never know how much he did for me.

I hastily handed a special friend, Rosemary Miller, my dawn outpourings and untidy writings and, cheerfully encouraging, she was always available for last minute typing and rearrangements. Her enthusiasm, her brightness, her efficient typing and her understanding will long glow within me as a warm light.

To my editor, Alison Lowry, my admiration knows no bounds, and my thanks are a hundredfold. She sorted, queried, arranged, organised and kept me to the point and grindstone, produced a baby daughter and still remained competent and efficient. It is through her and her quiet encouragement that this book is as it is.

Joan van Gogh found plants and painted long hours to keep up to date, and her skill and interest is evident in her exquisite work. She found out of season flowers and searched far and wide for perfect specimens to do justice to her meticulous pen and eye. I am filled with appreciation for the important part she played in this book.

A heartfelt thank you to those very special persons who watched over me and pushed me into a timetable, who mopped tears and helped me find new pathways and who held lights at the end of despairing tunnels – this book is for you all.

INTRODUCTION

We have to have herbs in our lives! There is so much appeal in the growing of herbs, be it for culinary purposes, a fragrant wealth of flowers, for the medicine chest, or simply as part of a garden's landscape. So many herbs are pleasing to the eye when seen growing in amongst other garden plants, while in containers herbs make aromatic ornaments for a window-box, stoep or patio. As they require so little time and effort, herbs make ideal pot-plants.

Folklore enthusiasts will be intrigued by the magic, myth and history behind these amazing plants. Once you start growing herbs you will find yourself becoming more and more fascinated and involved and you may even decide to start your own special collection. This can be an exciting hobby. You could start a collection of fragrant herbs and go on to collect pot-pourri recipes, perhaps even making and experimenting with your own combinations. Another idea is to put together a kitchen garden of rare food flavourings, such as the unusual salsify, or garlic chives or angelica. Always of interest are the specifically African herbs, particularly to South Africans, and indigenous plants placed in attractive positions will enhance any garden.

There is really no limit to the possible depth of your involvement with herbs. My own particular passion for thyme led me to discover several varieties available in South Africa: a golden variety, a silver queen and a woolly thyme, as well as various culinary types. It is useful to grow your herbs together in a bed for purposes of comparison and interest. Each should be well labelled and separated by paths or dividers.

However you grow your own herbs, there is one thing you can be sure of – the pleasure and interest you will get from them knows no bounds.

One thing which I am often asked to explain is the difference between a herb and a spice. Both groups of plants are used in medicine, cooking, perfume and commerce. Herbs and spices are often grouped together, and frequently confused, but there is a fundamental difference between the two which will enable the gardener to distinguish very quickly.

Herbs are those plants whose roots, stems, leaves, flowers, seeds and pods are used in some form – and they grow in a temperate zone.

Spices are plants used in a similar way but they grow in the tropics as they need continuous heat and moisture.

Should you wish to have a complete garden of both herbs and spices, you will probably be disappointed as their climatic requirements differ. In the warmer parts of South Africa, for example Natal's tropical zone, it is possible, however, to grow some herbs and spices together.

Perhaps never before has it been more important to know about our green heritage. We need to probe more deeply into alternative aspects of health and development, both spiritual and physical, and a knowledge of herbs and their uses can help us towards our own fulfilment.

Herbs give us more for the time and space devoted to them than any other plants. They are natural medicine chests and each and every one of us can derive some benefit from their amazing properties, whether used in our daily cup of tea, for flavouring our meals, as medicines or simply for their fragrance.

A herb garden can do many things – it may satisfy, inspire, uplift and revitalize. It can help us to overcome the deep stresses and worries we are prone to in our everyday lives. I could even go so far as to say that we dare not live without a herb or two close at hand.

There are other reasons for having herbs in the garden besides their culinary, medicinal and aromatic uses. Their scents are actually beneficial to other garden plants. There is less insect damage found in gardens where certain herbs have been interplanted and the healing qualities which so many herbs possess are often absorbed by ailing plants nearby. Certain herbs will attract bees and butterflies to your garden, while others act as insect repellents. Herbs can also be used to make your own garden sprays, infinitely preferable to using chemical sprays.

I cannot stress enough the importance of the many plants which grow readily and easily around us – the weeds that grow vigorously, the unexpected plants that simply pop up; we need those plants either to use in our diets or merely to absorb the fragrance or 'energy vibration' that they give off. The French herbalist Maurice Mességué, whose healing work with herbs is world renowned, said: 'People ascribe the greatest healing power to drugs that come from farthest away, drugs that cost the most. In my long experience I have come to believe that people go to the ends of the earth and look for something they could find right on their doorstep. If we could only learn to trust Nature!'

Undoubtedly there has lately been a resurgence of interest in herbal medicine. Patients and prospective patients as well as the medical profession itself no longer seem satisfied with the galaxy of man-made medicines available today. Why this should be is a complex issue and the morass of arguments surrounding it is confusing. One reason, however, is the increasing number of toxic effects resulting from the use of synthetic drugs.

Rudolf Hauschke, in his book *The Nature of Substance*, succinctly describes modern structural chemistry. Between 1858 and 1865 a well-known chemist and scientist, Kekulé, after many years of research, developed the concept of carbon atoms 'joining hands', which concept is the basis of structural chemistry which mirror-images nature. It was soon discovered that substances from this carbon group, produced at intermediate stages of dye manufacture, react on the human organism. Thus the era of synthetic drugs was ushered in. Salycylic preparations such as aspirin, which comes from the willow tree, were now produced from phenol, a white crystalline aromatic solid. This chemical therapy starting from a nucleus could then be turned to living plasma and the effects varied by adding side chains. These side products had amongst them sweet-tasting substances – the foundation of saccharines and nitro-benzol. A primary substance in this development was aromatic and so with ingenious synthesizing a wealth of artificial scents could be produced. In this way the synthetic perfume industry came into being, with its immense variety

THE SUB EARTHLY SPECTRUM OF SUBSTANCES
AS A MIRROR IMAGE OF NATURAL SUBSTANCES

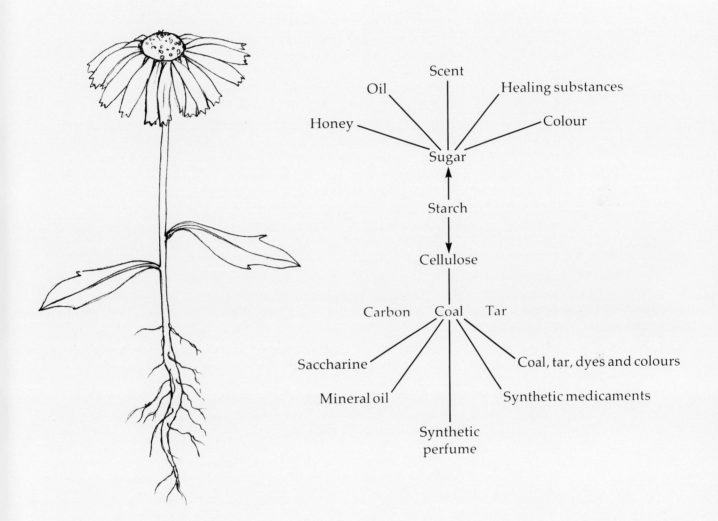

Scent

Oil   Healing substances

Honey   Colour

Sugar

↑

Starch

↓

Cellulose

Carbon   Coal   Tar

Saccharine   Coal, tar, dyes and colours

Mineral oil   Synthetic medicaments

Synthetic
perfume

of compounds, each imitating a different plant fragrance.

The whole carbon-coal-tar industry is a triumph of the human mind, but what of the spiritual, cosmic, vibrant life, the life force? Let us take a parallel: first the perfect natural plant – roots, stems, leaves and flowering top with its seed vessel, colourful petals, fragrant oils and honey in its stamens; then the carbon-coal-tar industry, its 'roots' giving synthetic sweeteners, perfumes, medications, dyes and colours and oils, and its 'flowering head' lost in the darkness of lifelessness.

Starch forms natural substances and this starchy matter is metamorphosed in the exhaling of the cosmic breath into sugars, flower colours, flower fragrances, honey, etheric oils and mecicinal therapeutic substances whose origin is deep within the plant. Downwards along the stem there is a gradual densifying and mineralising throug the cellulose until a biological zero is reached in carbon or coal-tar and in this place the human mind had taken hold of it and created its mirror-image in synthetic substances.

By contrasting these two realms we realize that the upper section is biological harmony, wholeness, health and beauty, living and growing and vibrantly alive, full of natural metamorphosing ranges that are endless; and below in the dark underworld is the ghostly reflection of God's cosmic creativity.

Using the life force of plants as medicine is the basis of homoeopathy and herbalism, for, by means of the plants, the sun's rays are transformed into flesh. Alone of all life forms plants can catch the sunlight and by their unique alchemy compound it with basic soil ingredients to make the food which sustains all living things.

I am not trying to replace the doctor, homoeopathic doctor or herbalist; I wish merely to draw attention to the natural goodness right here in our own gardens and fields and mountains. My advice is always to consult your doctor about serious ailments and be sure of the identification of a plant before you start a home treatment.

It was Thoreau who said: 'Heaven is not only above your head, it is under your feet as well.' In the pages which follow what I hope to do is bring alive a bit of that heaven which is under your feet. I want to take you by the hand and lead you along the paths of an enchanted garden and let you rediscover those plants which you have always known but which you will now look at with new eyes. I want to share their fragrances and tastes with you, and give you more than just fragrance and more than just taste. I want to impart to you my own love and delight in these natural wonders so that after we have walked through this herb garden you will never again be the same person as the one who turned these first pages.

1
DESIGNING AND PLANNING
THE HERB GARDEN

The laying out and style of a herb garden will be dictated by the people who are going to enjoy and use the plants. Formal or informal, a herb garden is a garden both to be used and to give pleasure.

As decorative plants, many herbs are not very popular but in the design of a traditional herb garden they have a certain appeal redolent of ancient times, which enhances the subtle beauty of these plants of benefit and blessing.

Most herbs are at their best on a site which is relatively protected from searing winds and frost; therefore low walls or fences that can accommodate climbing plants, or pergolas enclosing the area, are beneficial. In South Africa's heat and drought shady areas are a necessity and for this purpose pergolas are an excellent idea, as not only do they provide shade, but they also look beautiful covered with fragrant climbing roses, honeysuckle or jasmine. Shade-loving foxgloves, acanthus, buttercups, angelica and ferns also do well in the coolness.

It pays to spend time and energy clearing and digging the site for your herb garden and the crop of eager weeds which will probably appear after the initial work can easily be eradicated before the new herbs are planted. Ideally the site chosen should be in a sunny position and the soil should be fertile and drainage fairly good. Some form of moisture-retaining material such as a good compost should be dug in at an approximate ratio of 4 spadefuls of compost to 1 square metre of soil. *Never use artificial fertilizers or sprays on herbs as many of these plants are used for medicinal purposes.* Leaf mould or animal bedding straw can also be dug into the soil to provide moisture-retaining humus. For the midsummer South African heat mulching with leaves and grass to retain coolness and moisture is a good idea.

Whatever size of garden you are planning, level the site and lay the paths before planting. The gardener must be able to get to every part of the garden for easy maintenance. Do not make the paths too narrow; they should be wide enough to accommodate two people walking beside each other, for strolling through a herb garden, sharing it with another person, is one of its greatest pleasures. People need to touch and smell and see the plants close at hand. Paths can be paved, bricked, cemented, grassed or gravelled. Many traditional herb gardens had fine grass paths. This is possibly the cheapest way of making an attractive path, but it does need to be mowed regularly and clipped at the edges. Beds which are edged with stones or bricks will also keep the grass in check. Cost and your personal taste will determine the path material you choose. Paving stones and bricks make beautiful paths and these need a solid, well tramped down foundation. Gravel paths also require a good solid foundation as well as an edging of bricks to contain the gravel.

The simplest herb garden is a square or rectangle divided by crossed paths (traditionally used to scare the devil!), with a sundial in the centre. In a South African herb garden there are primarily four major sections. The ones I choose are a culinary section, an aromatic section, a medicinal section and an African indigenous section.

A good selection of culinary herbs would include the following:

Angelica	Coriander	Pumpkin
Anise	Crab-apple	Radish
Asparagus	Dill	Rhubarb
Balm	Fennel	Rosemary
Basil	Garlic	Sage
Bay	Ginger	Salad burnet
Bergamot	Granadilla	Savory
Borage	Lovage	Sorrel
Caraway	Lucerne	Strawberry
Celery	Marjoram	Tarragon
Chervil	Mint	Thyme
Chicory	Mustard	Watercress
Chives	Oreganum	
Comfrey	Parsley	

The aromatic section would have these herbs:

Balm	Honeysuckle	Pyrethrum
Bergamot	Hyssop	Rose
Carnations	Jasmine	Rosemary
Catnip	Lavender	Santolina
Dianthus	Lemon verbena	Southernwood
Gardenia	Mignonette	Tuberose
Geranium	Mints	Violet
Ginger	Mock orange	
Heliotrope	Myrtle	

Medicinal herbs include:

Acanthus	Golden-rod	Periwinkle
Ajuga	Grape	Pig's ear cotyledon
Amaranth	Hollyhock	Quince
Bergamot	Horehound	Rock-rose
Buttercup	Hydrangea	Rue
Calendula	Hypericum	Santolina
Castor-oil plant	Hyssop	Soapwort
Catnip	Iris	Sourfig
Chamomile	Ivy	Garden valerian
Columbine	Job's tears	Verbascum
Cornflower	Lavender	Vinca rosea
Elder	Maidenhair fern	Wormwood
Feverfew	Myrtle	Yarrow
Foxglove	Nasturtium	
Germander	Nettle	

Finally, the indigenous African section of herbs would include:

Agave	Eucomis	Prickly pear
Aloe	Geranium (scented	Pumpkin
Arum	indigenous)	Pyrethrum
Asparagus (wild)	Job's tears	Sourfig
Buttercup (indigenous)	Marigold	Wilde als
Castor-oil plant	Mint (wild aquatic)	
Chicory (wild)	Pig's ear cotyledon	

The designs of course can vary enormously, but because of the ancient lore surrounding these amazing plants I prefer to use the traditional designs that have their roots in ancient civilizations. In these designs knowledge of the past has been mingled with superstition, magic, folklore and astrology; it is only by comparing suggestions, however, and by your own trial and error that yours will be the garden of magic it is intended to be. A mature herb garden is an enviable possession but however small the garden, be it a window-box or tub on a sunny patio or balcony, herbs are within the reach of each one of us.

In my experience the most beautiful shape for a herb garden is square, with a central circular lawn (a pennyroyal mint or a daisy lawn) with the sundial or light centre in the middle. A larger circle surrounds the central one and here the insecticide plants, the old roses and the mints, can be grown in four sections separated by paths. Outside of this circular section are the four large sections containing the medicinal plants, the indigenous African plants, the aromatic and the culinary plants.

A speckled toad should be encouraged to live in each section to protect the young herbs and a rosemary bush planted in each corner repels the evil spirits. The devil does not like water so a couple of bird-baths or small ponds should be placed in attractive positions. Elder hedges will keep witches away but an elder tree at the entrance to your garden will do as well. The left horn of an ox can be burned on the shortest winter days to keep out the dark mists and frosts. Also at the entrance a pair of camphor trees can be planted; they are the trees of blessing and all who pass between them will be blessed – particularly a newborn baby!

Herbs for culinary use can be planted in hollow concrete blocks set into the soil and placed within easy reach of the kitchen door. These are neat, attractive and practical for those everyday flavouring herbs. A wagonwheel lying in the soil makes an unusual type of planter; the spaces between each spoke of the wheel can be used for a different herb – a good way to grow the rampant mints as it curbs their spread.

Low hedges can be made of lavender, rosemary, germander, santolina or southernwood and can be an attractive feature in any garden. Leave enough space for the roots so that they do not encroach upon the other herbs. All clippings can be kept for pot-pourris and herb teas.

There is no rule which says that herbs must only be grown in formal or patterned gardens. They will look just as beautiful growing freely. Interplanted with other perennials in a border, herbs create interesting patterns and the different textures and fragrances can make your garden a pure delight.

Several herbs make interesting ground covers, ajuga for instance, or creeping buttercup, the creeping thymes, violets and prunella. Some do well in shade while others, like creeping rosemary, are drought resistant and can cover a bank with greenness and fragrance in the most blazing sun. The sourfig, too, has a wonderful drought resistant quality; it always looks neat and trim and will cover unsightly stony places quickly and evenly.

The following are designs for twelve different herb gardens and these can be adapted to any size to fit any piece of ground. They are inspired by the old herb garden designs originating from the cloister gardens, the intricately designed formal knot gardens and the psychic gardens. All have the central position for a sundial and all can be surrounded by a path for easy access to all points.

The enlarged design is for me the ultimate in herb garden enjoyment and it is the design of my own garden. Although it takes up more space than the simpler designs, it, too, can be adjusted to smaller gardens. The outer boundary can be lined with pergolas – a most attractive touch, providing the necessary shade for hanging baskets of maidenhair ferns, commelinas, nasturtiums and other shade-loving herbs. I train morning glories, jasmine and honeysuckle up over the pergolas and the fragrance on a summer evening is almost unbelievable. A bench on a small paved area under the pergola makes a welcome resting place for visitors and I always place a bird-bath nearby; the birds soon get to know it is there.

Attractive tiles inscribed with pertinent sayings can be set into the paths or into an area near the benches. I have made clay inscriptions which read: 'He who plants a garden walks hand in hand with God' and 'The Lord has created medicine out of the earth and he who is wise will not abhor them'.

This old Irish blessing is a favourite of mine:

Sure and may there be a road before you and it bordered with roses the likes of which have never been smelt before, for the warm fine colour and the great sweetness that is in them.

Do label your herbs for quick reference and identification. There are numerous ways of doing this and you will choose the method which suits you best. I use a ceramic tile with a hole in it, hooking a thick wire rod through the hole and then pressing it into the ground. On the tiles I carve the herb's common name, its Latin name and its major uses.

Growing herbs in containers has many advantages. A few small plants in an attractive container can often be better displayed than in the larger garden beds where they sometimes tend to get lost. Almost every type of herb can be grown in a container if given proper soil, the right amount of sun and water and enough room to grow. For herbs with long tap roots be sure that the container is deep enough.

With so many planters available, ranging from the old-fashioned clay pots, strawberry jars or huge asbestos tubs and barrels, from wooden planters to unusual distinctive jars and bowls, choosing the right ones is largely a matter of personal taste. Be sure, however, that your planters have good drainage holes so that the roots do not become waterlogged. Do choose a big enough planter if you want to group herbs together. Hanging baskets are suitable for the creeping thymes and creeping rosemary, and even chives look good from aloft. A basket hanging outside the kitchen door can be most useful for the busy cook.

Window-boxes can serve the needs of the flat-dweller quite adequately: one plant

THE IDEAL GARDEN

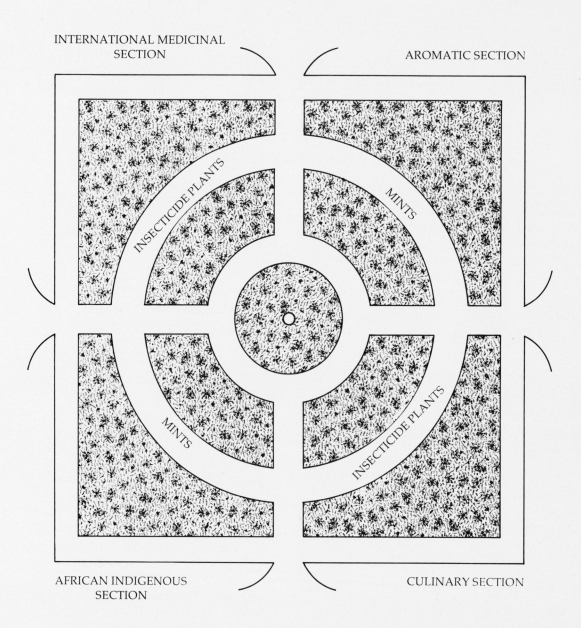

INTERNATIONAL MEDICINAL SECTION

AROMATIC SECTION

INSECTICIDE PLANTS

MINTS

MINTS

INSECTICIDE PLANTS

AFRICAN INDIGENOUS SECTION

CULINARY SECTION

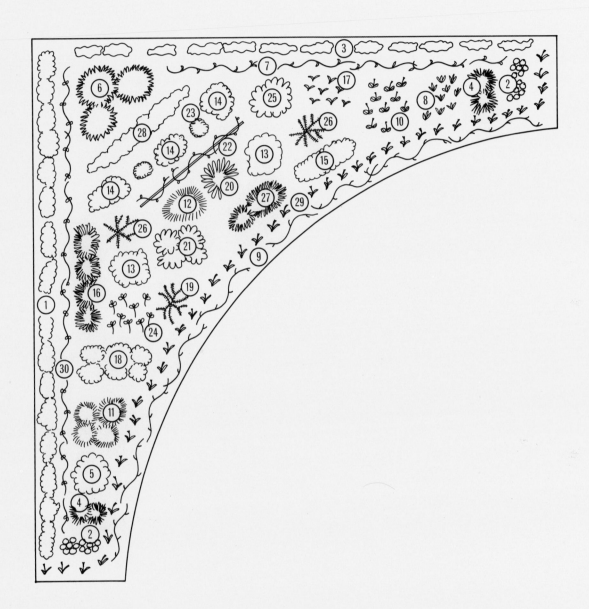

1	Ajuga border	11 Cornflower	21	Hydrangea
2	Acanthus	12 Quince	22	Ivy on small trellis
3	Catnip border	13 Crab apple	23	Maidenhair under shade
4	Vinca rosea	14 Elder	24	periwinkle
5	Soapwort	15 Feverfew	25	Rock rose
6	Bergamot	16 Foxglove	26	Rue
7	Calendula	17 Golden rod	27	Vinca (periwinkle)
8	Celery	18 Hollyhock	28	Wormwood
9	Strawberry border	19 Horehound	29	Yarrow
10	Columbine	20 Hypericum	30	Germander

AROMATIC SECTION

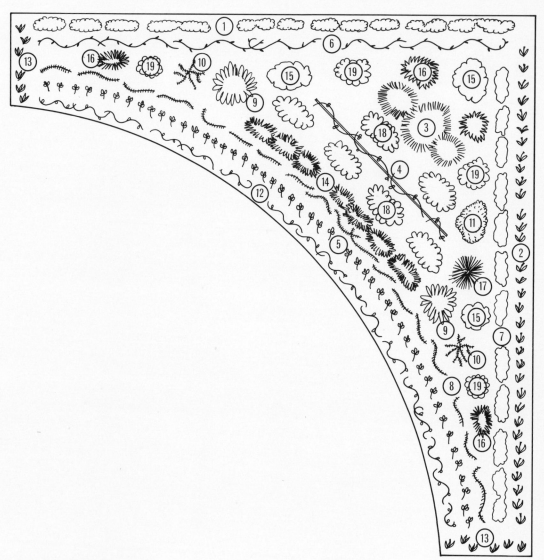

1 Lemon thyme border
2 Violets
3 Myrtle
4 Trellis of honeysuckle
5 Bergamot
6 Lavender variety
7 Another lavender variety
8 Scented geranium
9 Lemon verbena
10 Ginger
11 Anise
12 Border of pennyroyal or mentha repens

13 Iris
14 Hyssop
15 Mignonette
16 Rosemary
17 Chamomile
18 Varieties of fragrant mints
     (eau de cologne)
     (spearmint)
     (applemint)
     (peppermint)
19 Rose (four times)

CULINARY SECTION

1	Bay tree	12	Borage	23	Mustard
2	Parsley border	13	Celery	24	Nettle
3	Culinary thyme	14	Caraway	25	Oregano
4	Lemon thyme	15	Chicory	26	Radish
5	Majoram	16	Comfrey	27	Rhubarb
6	Sage	17	Dill	28	Salad burnet
7	Creeping rosemary	18	Fennel	29	Savory, winter and summer
8	Mints	19	Garlic	30·	Sorrel
9	Chives	20	Lovage	31	Tarragon
10	Lemon balm	21	Rosemary	32	Angelica
11	Basil	22	Lucerne	33	Chervil in shade of Bay

1 Agave	11 Trellis of grapes
2 Border of Aloes	12 Trellis of granadillas
3 Amaranth	13 Job's tears
4 Castor oil	14 Nasturtium
5 Arum border	15 Pig's ear cotyledon
6 Asparagus	16 Prickly pear
7 Sour fig border	17 Pumpkin
8 Wild chicory	18 Wilde als
9 Eucomis	19 Buttercup
10 2 borders scented geraniums	

INNER CIRCLES

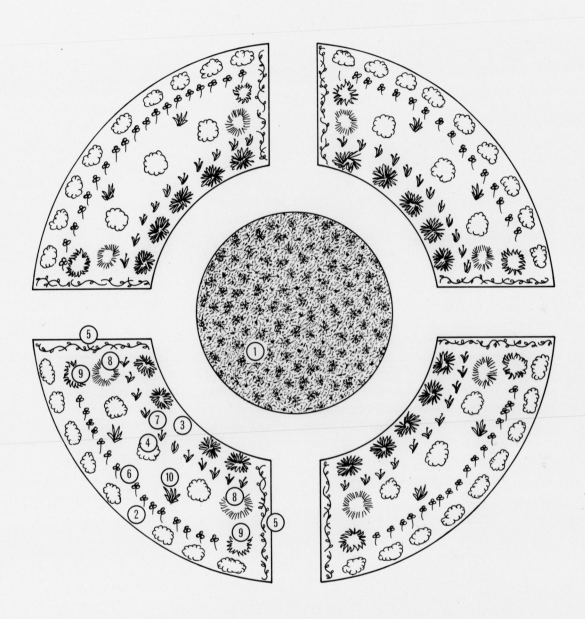

1   Lawn of pennyroyal or creeping chamomile
2   Rosemary (to repel the evil spirits!)
3   Southernwood
4   Roses – either old fashioned or Crimson Glory
5   Pyrethrum – path edging
6   Tansy
7   Marigold
8   Santolina
9   Valerian (garden)
10 Verbascum

each of thyme, marjoram and parsley, a tiny rosemary bush, with a small group of chives and perhaps a little creeping oreganum, will be sufficient for most people's culinary needs. Provided that the box gets a minimum of eight hours of sun a day and the plants get sufficient water this miniature herb garden should give many hours of pleasure.

Before putting in your herbs cover the holes at the bottom of your container with small stones or pieces of broken pot. Then use a good potting soil mixture to fill the container. One good mixture is:

7 parts garden soil
3 parts peat
1 part sand
3 parts good compost

Correct watering is an important aspect of container growing because water evaporates rapidly through the sides of the pot, if it is a clay or wooden pot or even an asbestos container. In very hot weather, therefore, your herbs will need a daily if not twice daily watering. Never allow the pot to dry out completely as this will damage the plant, considerably stunting its growth and causing it to wilt and die back. A good idea is to stand the pot in a bowl of shallow water; this way the water is absorbed through the bottom of the pot. Extra attention must be paid to hanging baskets as they tend to dry out more quickly. Unless you are growing herbs for their flower-heads and seeds, cut off the flowers as they appear so that all the goodness can be stored in the leaves.

Every two weeks or so add a concentrated plant food to your container of herbs; this will ensure lush and beautiful plants that will stand a lot of picking. I would advise using the natural seaweed and organic plant food concentrates to keep the herbs healthy, pure and uncontaminated. Remember that many of the herbs will be used in medicinal preparations so never use artificial or chemical sprays, fertilizers or fumigants.

Planned with thought and care, your herb garden, whether it be a large traditional one or a window-box on a balcony, will become a priceless treasure, ever fascinating and ever changing.

2
100 INDIVIDUAL PLANTS

ACANTHUS

PLATE 1

Family:	*Acanthaceae*
Species:	*Acanthus mollis* (bear's breeches)
Plant:	perennial
Height:	up to 1 metre
Soil:	cool, moist, loam
Exposure:	shade
Propagation:	division, seeds
Uses:	landscape, medicinal
Meaning:	artifice

Acanthus is a much loved garden plant which thrives in the shady areas under trees. Its stalk (up to 120 cm in height) and flower spikes can be most striking in large summer flower arrangements and they will last a long time. The beautiful ovate, glossy leaves of *Acanthus mollis* are said to have inspired the designs for the decoration of the Corinthian marble columns in classical Greek architecture.

The leaves were also once used as an application for burns and scalds. They were crushed and warmed in hot water, then applied to the burn and held in place with lint and bandages. Nowadays, however, acanthus is used as a decorative garden plant or pot-plant only. It may be planted in a large tub filled with rich, loamy, well-composted soil, and it will make a beautiful addition to a shady stoep or patio; it is even a successful indoor plant if given enough light.

If you are planting acanthus in the garden, divide up clumps in spring and plant 60 cm apart in well-composted, deeply dug, loamy soil in the shade. Keep well watered until thoroughly established. Thereafter water deeply once a week and you will have many years of pleasure from their rich bottle-green, handsome leaves.

Seeds can be sown successfully if you use fresh seed. Sow individually 5 cm apart in a sand and compost mixture of equal parts. Keep cool and moist and cover the sand tray with a sheet of glass until the seedlings are up. Plant out once the seedlings are big enough to handle into a rich, well-dug bed into which has been dug a generous application of compost and old manure. Space them 60 cm apart.

AGAVE

PLATE 1

Family:	*Agavaceae*
Species:	*Agave americana* (century plant, garingboom)
Plant:	perennial until it flowers
Height:	1 – 3 metres
Soil:	poor, dry
Exposure:	full sun
Propagation:	seeds, suckers
Uses:	medicinal, decorative

Choose the site for your century plant carefully. It is a wonderfully useful plant and very decorative. It has a long lifespan, up to ten years, and it flowers only once, sending out a huge flowering stalk. Once that has set seed, the plant dies – almost like a swansong in this final flowering.

A leaf split and warmed is a local application for rheumatism but take care to test this on a small area of your skin first as the juice can be an irritant, producing a burning sensation on skin contact. Softened, peeled leaves are also used as a dressing for burns and an infusion of the leaf is a strong purgative. Use chopped leaves to fill one cup, pour over 250 ml (1 cup) boiling water and allow to cool before drinking.

Agaves grow just about anywhere, seeming almost to prefer arid soil conditions. Sow the seed where it is to grow and plant 180 cm apart, keeping moist until the seed germinates. Often you will find germinated, strongly growing small agaves still attached to the flowering branches, especially after late summer rains. These need only be placed on soil that has been dug over and watered and they will soon send down roots.

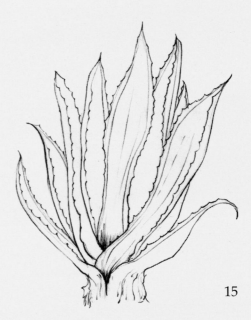

15

AJUGA

PLATE 2

Family: *Labiatae*
Species: *Ajuga aphrydis* (carpet bugle)
Plant: perennial
Height: low growing ground cover
Soil: any
Exposure: partial shade
Propagation: division
Uses: landscape, medicinal

Ajuga will make a lovely edging to the beds along a path in your herb garden or planted around stepping stones. It is an even, neat ground cover and there are several varieties, some of which have beautiful multi-coloured leaves. Ajuga thrives in the shade but in full sun seems to dry off in patches. It sends up pretty blue flower spikes from October to January (when it is in the shade I have found flower spikes almost throughout the year) and it does especially well if watered regularly.

The roots of ajuga can be boiled and the brew used to bathe skin rashes – 250 ml (1 cup) roots to 2 litres (8 cups) water. Boil for 10 minutes, cool and strain, and use several times daily on the rash.

Ajuga can also be combined with elder leaves and flowers to make a soothing wash for eczema and heat rash. Combine 250 ml (1 cup) ajuga roots, 500 ml (2 cups) elder leaves, and 250 ml (1 cup) elder flowers in 2 litres (8 cups) water. Boil for 15 minutes, cool, then strain and keep in the refrigerator. Wash the afflicted area twice daily with this comforting brew and dab on with cotton-wool several times during the day.

With all brews and decoctions always test a small area first for burning, irritation or inflammation before proceeding. In rare instances instead of soothing the area it may irritate it and in that case wash with clear water, or dab with fresh milk, until the irritation is gone.

Established plants can be divided in spring and replanted in well-dug soil into which 4 spadefuls of compost to 1 square metre have been worked. Space them 20 cm apart and keep moist until they are well established.

Do not use the variegated or hybridised species medicinally; the old-fashioned variety is the best.

ALOE

PLATE 2

Family:	*Liliaceae*
Species:	*Aloe davyana, A. ferox*
Plant:	perennial
Height:	up to 30 cm
Soil:	poor
Exposure:	sun
Propagation:	seeds
Uses:	landscape, medicinal
Meaning:	grief

Aloe davyana has to have a place in South African herb gardens. Not only are its medicinal uses amazing, but it is also highly decorative. Its pink flower-heads lend a soft attractive colour to the bleak buffs and browns of the winter veld; they also last well in water and can be used as a winter decoration.

Medicinally, the juice obtained from the *Aloe davyana* is a soothing local application for burns and sores, as well as an African snake-bite remedy. The chopped up leaf can also be applied as a dressing to a suppurating sore by placing the juice and leaf on a bandage and binding it in place; the dressing should be changed frequently.

The juice of many aloe species, particularly *Aloe ferox*, is dried and exported all over the world as a purgative. Use 2 – 3 pinches of the dried juice in 150 ml (½ cup) warm milk and sweeten with honey or molasses. This is an effective treatment for expelling worms, and relieving constipation and indigestion. However, as it acts on the large intestine, drawing blood to the area, it should not be prescribed or used for anyone suffering from piles.

Externally the juice can be applied to burns, scalds, rashes, mouth ulcers and heat rash. First shave off the spiked borders of the leaf and cut the leaf crossways; then apply the fresh, sticky juice directly to the area. You will find it extremely bitter but if it can be tolerated it is a sure healer for mouth ulcers.

Seeds should be planted in spring in sand-filled trays. They germinate quickly and easily and need only to be kept moist until big enough to handle. The plants need sun from an early age so make sure the seedlings get enough warmth and light until they are established, then plant out 30 cm apart in well-dug soil to which a little old manure has been added. Thereafter they need only an occasional watering. In areas of heavy frost the flower may suffer damage but on the whole aloes are tough and undemanding.

AMARANTHUS

PLATE 2

Family:	*Amaranthaceae*
Species:	*Amaranthus hypochondriacus* (prince's feather),
	A. caudatus (love-lies-bleeding)
Plant:	annual, sometimes biennial
Height:	up to 1 metre
Soil:	any
Exposure:	sun, partial shade
Propagation:	seeds
Uses:	culinary, medicinal
Meaning:	affectation

Amaranthus hypochondriacus is one of a number of amaranthus species which makes an unusual and interesting garden plant. Most amaranthus species are native to tropical countries where they are used as pot herbs. The name derives from the Greek *amaranton*, which means 'not fading', as the long crimson flowers, often called 'lamb's tails' or 'bleeding heart', do not fade when the plant dies; thus the amaranth came to symbolise immortality.

The young leaves make a delicious spinach cooked in just a little water and served with a squeeze of lemon juice, salt and a dab of butter. They can also be included in salads and soups.

The herb is astringent and as such can be used in the treatment both of diarrhoea and anaemia. Externally, it may be used as a wash for ulcers, and it is also a wonderful gargle and mouth-wash for mouth ulcers. In addition it reduces tissue swelling and makes an excellent douche for leucorrhoea. The same brew can be used to treat all these ailments. It is made by pouring 500 ml (2 cups) boiling water over 250 ml (1 cup) leaves. Allow to stand, then pour off and drink the liquid. Take 12,5 ml (1 tbls) six times a day for diarrhoea. Use the same wash for ulcers, douching and gargling.

Do not weed out other amaranthus species from the garden; they all make an excellent strengthening, blood-building tonic in cases of anaemia.

The amaranthus grows wild, seeming to prefer waste places and roadsides, but it also grows easily from seed sown in spring. Sow in sand-filled seed trays, cover with a light layer of sand and compost and keep fairly moist. When the seedlings are big enough to handle plant out 30–45 cm apart in a prepared bed which has had a little well-rotted manure added to it. Shade the seedlings in their new position for a few days and keep well watered. Once the seedlings are established water them once a week.

1

2

1 Acanthus *p 14*
2 Agave *p 15*

3

2

1

1 Ajuga *p 16*
2 Aloe *p 17*
3 Amaranthus *p 18*

ANGELICA

PLATE 3

Family:	*Umbelliferae*
Species:	*Angelica archangelica*
Plant:	biennial
Height:	120–180 cm
Soil:	light alkaline
Exposure:	semi-shade
Propagation:	seeds
Uses:	culinary

Tall stately angelica is perhaps best placed at the back of the garden.

The herb was called angelica in medieval times because of its healing properties. Today it is best known as the pieces of green candied decorations used on cakes or in confectionery. These are obtained in the following way: Cut thick stems, discarding leaves and roots, and place in a saucepan. Pour over a brine made of 1 litre (4 cups) water and 50 ml (4 tbls) salt and bring to the boil. Boil for 10 minutes and drain. Rinse the stems under running water in a sieve and, with a sharp knife, scrape away the tough, fibrous outer skin. Cut into 10 cm lengths.

To process 450 g (1 lb) angelica make a syrup using 450 g (1 lb) sugar and 600 ml (1 pt) water. Boil together for 10 minutes. Next add the angelica and boil for 20 minutes. Using a slotted spoon, remove the angelica from the syrup and drain on a wire rack. Cover the syrup and set aside.

Next dry the angelica, first covering it in greaseproof paper, then placing a kitchen towel over it and letting it stand in the sun for 1 – 3 days or until it feels dry to the touch. Then again boil up the syrup, add the angelica and boil for 20 minutes or until most of the syrup has been absorbed. Remove the angelica from the syrup, drain and place in a cool oven (110°C) overnight. When it is dry sprinkle with sugar and store in an airtight jar in a cool dark place.

Angelica stems can also be cooked with rhubarb to reduce the acidity as the latter has a sweetening quality. Finely chopped angelica can also be used in fruit salads. The midribs of the large leaves can be eaten like celery and the seeds can be used in spice mixtures. Ground seeds are used as a fixative in perfumery.

Angelica does best in a light alkaline soil, although I have also grown it in black turf quite satisfactorily. Seeds should be sown in spring. Angelica needs light shade in the heat of our African sun and during summer is prone to aphid attack. Any of the aphid sprays discussed in Chapter 9 will be effective. Plant seedlings out in well-composted soil, 120 cm apart. Water well and keep shaded until established.

Angelica flowers in its second year and if the flowers are clipped off it will go on flowering for several years. Once the plant has flowered it begins to die so it can really be pulled up at this stage. If the seeds look mature they can be planted at once in time for the next season. The leaves and stems can be chopped up and dried and used in pot-pourris as a fixative.

19

ANISE

PLATE 3

Family: *Umbelliferae*
Species: *Pimpinella anisum*
Plant: annual
Height: 60 cm
Soil: light, fairly rich
Exposure: full sun
Propagation: seeds
Uses: culinary, medicinal

Anise is a confectioner's herb and is delicious for flavouring liqueurs. The seeds can be used in seed-cakes in the same way as caraway seeds are used. Anise was once used in the making of aniseed cakes which were eaten by the Romans after a feast; this cake is thought to be the forerunner of our traditional wedding cake.

Anise is also beneficial for digestive disorders, and a seed or two can be chewed for relief of heartburn, indigestion and flatulence. The leaves can be chopped into salads but should be used very sparingly as their flavour is strong.

Sow fresh seed in spring in trays and transplant the seedlings to a light soil with plenty of compost as they seem to need a fairly constant supply of water. The plant has a tap root so it does not transplant easily. I find an egg box the most suitable for anise seedlings. Fill it with sand, sow each seed individually and keep damp until the seedlings appear. When they are big enough tear away the already disintegrating egg box and plant them, cardboard and all, in the garden, keeping them shaded for a couple of days. In this way the egg box breaks down in the soil and the roots are not disturbed. Plant the seedlings 60 cm apart and in the summer's growth use the lower leaves for flavouring, cutting them close to the stem.

ARUM LILY

PLATE 3

Family: *Araceae*
Species: *Zantedeschia aethiopica*, *Z. pentlandii* (golden arum)
Plant: perennial
Height: up to 1,5 m
Soil: rich, moist
Exposure: partial shade, shade
Propagation: tubers, seeds
Uses: medicinal, decorative
Meaning: forsaken

Arums need moisture and they will grow lush and tall along the edges of ponds or streams. There are about ten species of *Zantedeschia* endemic in Africa, seven of which occur in the Transvaal. Many die down in winter but the white arum lily can withstand frost if protected by trees. It is really only this common white arum which is used medicinally and whose tuber is edible. Its leaf is soothing for burns and insect bites and it draws out sores and boils. Wash and warm the leaf and then bind it over the affected area overnight. The next day a new leaf can be applied if the boil or sore has not drawn well.

Zantedeschia pentlandii is the well-known commercial golden arum but this should not be used medicinally.

Although they can take sun, arums do best in the shade and they will make an eye-catching addition to a shady place in your herb garden. Prepare a bed with compost and well-aged manure. Dig deeply and loosen the ground to a depth of 30 cm, then place the tubers in a circle 30 cm apart, cover with soil and keep moist.

Fresh seed can be quickly and easily grown in seed trays. Press the large seeds into wet sand, cover with sand and keep well watered. Plant out into a group when big enough to handle, keeping a distance of 30 cm between each plant.

The more often you cut the flowers, the more your plant will produce, but do take care when handling them as there is a skin irritant present in the juice which, if taken into the mouth, causes a burning sensation and swelling of the mucous membranes.

ASPARAGUS

PLATE 4

Family:	*Liliaceae*
Species:	*Asparagus officinalis*, *A. plumosis*
Plant:	perennial
Height:	plumes up to 1 metre
Soil:	moist, rich
Exposure:	sun
Propagation:	division, seeds
Uses:	culinary, medicinal

Asparagus is an amazing medicinal plant which has been cultivated for over two thousand years. It is a marvellous general tonic for the system so eat as much of it as you like during spring. It is partially beneficial for the urinary system (gall-bladder, jaundice and kidney infections), as well as heart disease and flatulence. Water in which the shoots have been boiled is a rheumatism soother, while the root and the small berry-like fruits are used as diuretics.

Keep an eye out for the wild *Asparagus plumosus* for it, too, has wonderful medicinal properties and the slender green shoots are delicious to eat.

A tea made from this asparagus species is beneficial for rheumatism and pulmonary tuberculosis. Use 12,5 ml (1 tbls) leaves and young shoots to 250 ml (1 cup) boiling water, steep and strain. Sweeten with honey and to obtain relief drink half a cupful morning and night.

The well-known garden asparagus, *A. officinalis*, can be started in August by planting crowns which are available from seed houses and nurseries. These need well-dug, well-composted, loamy soil. Plant each crown in a hole approximately 15 cm deep, cover with soil and press down. Then water well and do not allow to dry out before the buds appear above the surface.

In the first two seasons allow the crowns to become well established before cutting the shoots. Tall, feathery plumes will emerge which must be cut back in mid-summer to encourage new shoots to form. After two years build up the earth around the asparagus crown, again in August. This is to elongate the bud or shoot and to blanch it. When it is about 15–20 cm high cut it at the base with a sharp knife.

Cook the asparagus by boiling it in salted water to which a good squeeze of lemon juice has been added (save the water for stock for soups).

To propagate in early spring divide up the crowns after four years of growth. New pieces need to be replanted at least 60 cm apart and nurtured during the first months until they are well established. Water deeply once a week.

Asparagus can also be grown successfully from seed but you will need to be patient as it will be several years before you can cut your first crop. Sow seed in trays in moist sand and cover with a sheet of glass. Keep warm and moist and only remove the glass when the seedlings are well up and vigorous. Plant into bags when big enough to handle and keep moist and well composted. The seedlings prefer a rich, friable soil at this stage to develop their crowns. Let them become sturdy in the bags or large pots before planting out into the garden. It is a good idea to choose a bed to one side of the herb garden to allow the asparagus to remain undisturbed for some years. Each year dig in compost and well-rotted manure around the crowns and water well during August before the spring growth.

BASIL

PLATE 4

Family:	*Labiatae*
Species:	*Ocimum basilicum*
Plant:	annual
Height:	30 – 60 cm
Soil:	average
Exposure:	sun, but semi-shade in midsummer
Propagation:	seeds
Uses:	culinary, medicinal
Meaning:	hatred

Sweet basil is the herb most popular for culinary purposes, but another type, dark opal, is fast becoming a favourite in the garden as it is decorative and can be used as a substitute for ordinary basil in cooking.

Basil must be one of the most rewarding of herbs to grow as it has so many uses. Bunches hung in the kitchen will keep flies away, while dried stalks burnt on an evening fire in winter keep mosquitoes at bay. It also has a medicinal use: for clearing mouth infections it can be used as a gargle – 6 leaves to 250 ml (1 cup) boiling water. Crushed, pounded leaves are said to stimulate hair growth if massaged well into the scalp.

A lovely way of storing fresh basil is to pick a quantity of leaves in midsummer and put them in layers in a crock, covering each layer with coarse salt (not treated or iodised salt). Each day fresh leaves can be added and covered with more salt until the crock is full. Then cover the crock and keep it in a cool place. When a recipe calls for basil a leaf or two can be taken out, shaken free of salt, washed and used as you would use freshly picked basil.

Basil dries easily. I wait until the winter frost is almost due (basil is susceptible to frost damage) and then pull up the whole plant and dry it on a rack in the shade. I then strip the crumbling leaves from the stems and store them for kitchen use. The seed-heads are ideal for pot-pourris as they give off a lovely clove-scent.

Another way to store basil is to pack it into bottles and cover with olive oil. It keeps indefinitely and makes a delicious flavour-filled salad dressing.

Basil germinates easily from seeds and these can be sown in trays in August and kept protected until all danger of frost is past. Once the seedlings reach the four-leaf stage they can be transplanted easily. Place them 50 cm apart and keep them shaded for a day or two. The newly planted out seedlings do well with a little extra compost to keep the roots cool. They also need to be watered regularly to ensure lush succulent growth. Basil makes an easy pot-plant for a sunny window-sill in winter.

BAY

PLATE 4

Family: *Lauraceae*
Species: *Laurus nobilis*
Plant: perennial
Height: up to 4 metres
Soil: average, good drainage
Exposure: sun
Propagation: cuttings
Uses: culinary, medicinal, preservative, antiseptic
Meaning: glory

Traditions connected with the bay tree go back for centuries. It has a reputation of long standing as a protective tree against witchcraft, lightning and all evil, and bay leaves were the foliage used to make the original laurel wreaths, the emblem of distinction or victory which crowned poets and scholars. A laurel wreath is still used today for honouring symphony conductors and sportsmen of outstanding achievement.

Most herbs give their fragrance or flavour only fleetingly to the dishes to which they are added, but bay enriches and enhances for a long time and this is why it is such a useful addition to slow cooking beans, soups and stews.

Bay is an evergreen. Fresh leaves are available all year round for culinary use. Bay has antiseptic and preservative qualities which is why it was included in many meat dishes long ago. Even today it is included in bottled pickles, patés and potted meats.

The berries make a soothing rub for sprains and bruises. But, they are poisonous if eaten. They are said to bring about abortion in pregnant women.

Bay is an ingredient used in a bouquet garni and dried leaves and twigs burned on the fire during winter will serve as an antiseptic aid, clearing the air of germs.

A tub of bay at the kitchen door is not only decorative but useful as well. Plant a ring of parsley around it as an added attraction. It does need sun for the best part of the day, however, so choose your site with care.

In cold areas the bay laurel seldom flowers and, particularly while the tree is still small, it will need some winter protection. The plant grows slowly at first and then vigorously until it reaches tree proportions. It makes an ideal container plant – but be generous with the pot as it likes to have plenty of room to grow undisturbed.

Take cuttings at any time of the year from last season's growth by pulling off a small heel at the base of the stem. Dip into a rooting hormone. Plant the cuttings in boxes and keep them well watered and in a cool atmosphere. Often a plastic covering for the box is a good idea: make a 'tent' out of clear plastic, supported on wires so that it is held away from the plants and will not disturb them. This provides a greenhouse-type atmosphere which is beneficial to rooting. Allow the box of cuttings to harden off in the sun for a week or two before transplanting them directly into the garden. Leave plenty of space between them as in frost-free areas a bay tree can grow to enormous proportions.

BERGAMOT

Family:	*Labiatae*
Species:	*Monarda didyma* (bee balm, oswego tea)
Plant:	perennial
Height:	30–90 cm
Soil:	moist, fairly rich
Exposure:	sun, partial shade
Propagation:	cuttings, division
Uses:	fragrance, culinary, medicinal

Bergamot belongs in every garden as it is so easily grown and its flowers come in such a variety of colours that it gives pleasure wherever it grows. Bergamot is a good companion for rosemary and together they make an attractive hedge. Place the bergamot behind the rosemary for best effect as the tall flowering heads only have a summer's glory and will be cut back to ground level in winter.

Fresh bergamot leaves can be used to make a delicious tea or cool drink. Pour a litre (4 cups) of boiling water over a small handful of leaves and allow to steep. It may be drunk either hot or cold, sweetened with honey. The American Red Indians called it 'oswego tea' and used it as something of a cure-all, from wound washing to an indigestion rectifier, from a hairdressing lotion to the drawing of abscesses.

The red-flowered bergamot, *Monarda didyma*, is the one to be used medicinally. It is excellent for relief of nausea, flatulence and abdominal pain; it can also be inhaled in water to clear a cold in the nose or bronchitis and a leaf can be chewed to soothe a sore throat.

Divide the clump every 3 or 4 years and space 60 cm apart. Cuttings should be taken from the outer edges of the clump and set in sand to root quickly. Cut back the flowering heads to level with the lower leaves of the root stock when they have finished flowering and save the leaves and flowers for use in pot-pourris as they retain their fragrance beautifully. The winter growth is slow and will benefit from a dressing of compost. Take care not to let the plants dry out or they will become spindly and weak.

BORAGE

PLATE 5

Family:	*Boraginaceae*
Species:	*Borago officinalis*
Plant:	annual
Height:	30–90 cm
Soil:	dry, poor
Exposure:	sun, partial shade
Propagation:	seeds
Uses:	culinary, medicinal
Meaning:	courage

Borage heads a whole range of interesting plants and is so full of goodness we should make far more use of it than we do. Others in this 'hairy' family include comfrey, anchusa and forget-me-not. Most have mauve or blue flowers and no fragrance other than a fresh cucumber-like scent and taste.

Medicinally borage is used to bring down a fever and a brew made from the leaves is excellent for relieving inflamed, tired eyes. Use 4 leaves and 4–8 flowers in 250 ml (1 cup) boiling water. Stand for an hour, strain and use. Leaves can be rubbed onto insect bites and stings and crushed leaves applied to swellings and bruises will help to heal them. Borage contains potassium which helps the body make cortisone by stimulating the adrenal cortex. It is also useful in kidney and bladder infections. In medieval times it was said that wine with borage flowers in it would give strength and joyfulness and cure the fever.

Borage flowers can be preserved by crystallising and they make an attractive decoration on cakes and puddings. Dip each flower into the white of an egg which has been beaten with a fork until opaque but not foaming. Then dip into castor sugar. Turn until the flower is completely coated. (I leave a piece of stem on the flower for easier handling, and snip it off after it has dried.) Lay the flowers on a sheet of greaseproof paper on a wire rack and leave to dry in a warm place; alternatively place them in the oven at a very low heat, leaving the door slightly ajar. Once the flowers are dry and brittle, store in an airtight container between layers of greaseproof paper.

Borage also makes a delicious addition to fruit cups and fruit salads. A cup of borage tea, sweetened with honey, is a wonderful bedtime drink. It is made by pouring boiling water over 4 leaves and allowing to steep.

Borage seeds itself readily and seems to grow equally well in either clay or sandy soil. In the heat of midsummer I have found those borage plants which have seeded themselves under the filtered shade of nearby shrubs do far better than those in full sun, so keep a few seedlings for a cooler part of the garden in summer. Borage also does well as a pot-plant and is wonderful for attracting bees, but it is difficult to transplant once it reaches the four-leaf stage as it has a long tap root. Seeds do not germinate in the coldest months but in spring the seedlings pop up everywhere.

Seeds can be sown separately as soon as they are big enough to handle. Plant them

30–36 cm apart in tilled earth, about 1 cm below the surface, and cover with sand and a light dressing of compost to help keep the soil damp. Sow in early spring and again in midsummer.

Borage really can only be used fresh as it loses all its flavour when dried. At the end of the summer new, self-sown seedlings can be potted up for the kitchen window-sill for a continuous supply of leaves all winter to use in soups and fritters.

If you like bees grow a row of borage as they love the borage flowers.

BUTTERCUP

PLATE 5

Family:	*Ranunculaceae*
Species:	*Ranunculus multifidus*
Plant:	perennial
Height:	ground cover, other varieties up to 60 cm
Soil:	moist, rich
Exposure:	partial shade
Propagation:	runners
Uses:	medicinal, landscape
Meaning:	ingratitude

Ranunculus comes from *rana*, the Latin word for 'frog', a reference to some aquatic species. In the herb garden the buttercup can become very invasive unless it is checked, but it is a lovely ground cover which spreads quickly and easily.

For coughs, colds and mucous formation a tea can be made of the leaves and flowers. Use 12,5 ml (1 tbls) chopped leaves and flowers to 500 ml (2 cups) boiling water, allow to stand, then strain and drink a wineglassful three times a day.

A comforting poultice for sore throats and swollen glands can be made from the leaves: pour hot water over a bowl of leaves, apply the hot leaves to the area, cover with a towel and keep replacing with hot leaves until relief is felt. Do this twice daily or whenever necessary.

If planted in well-dug, well-composted, rich soil, and kept well watered, ranunculus will give many years of growth and pleasure and need only be kept within bounds. Take runners and replant them, taking care to keep them moist. In no time they will root well and spread. Plant about 30 cm apart in a shady part of the garden.

The taller varieties like the same conditions but need to be planted 30 cm apart. Their flowering stems can be cut back after the seeds have been set in autumn.

CALENDULA

Family:	*Compositae*
Species:	*Calendula officinalis* (pot marigold)
Plant:	annual
Height:	20–30 cm
Soil:	rich
Exposure:	sun, but does not mind afternoon shade
Propagation:	seeds
Uses:	medicinal, culinary
Meaning:	grief

Calendula is known as 'the herb of the sun' and this bright winter plant is the marigold referred to in old herbals. The botanical name comes from the Latin *calends* or *calendulae*, meaning 'throughout the months', which is intended to emphasise its long flowering period. It has single and double forms and the flowers close at night or on rainy days. If you keep your own seed the doubles can in a few seasons revert to the single form flowers, but as this does not affect the medicinal value it need not matter. However, as it is a showy plant in the herb garden and a calendula border is an eye catcher, some people prefer the double forms.

The petals of the calendula give colour to soups, gravies, stews and casseroles, and they can also be added to cakes and custards because of their delicate flavour, enhanced by a little vanilla. The following is a favourite recipe of mine:

MARIGOLD CAKES

125 ml (½ cup) sugar
100 g (½ cup) butter
12 ml (2½ tsp) baking powder
2 eggs, beaten
500 ml (2 cups) flour
1 ml (¼ tsp) salt
petals from 3 calendulas
2 ml (½ tsp) vanilla essence

Cream butter and sugar. Add eggs, calendula petals and dry ingredients. Beat well. Drop teaspoonfuls of the mixture onto a greased baking sheet. Bake at 180°C (350°F) for 10 minutes or until lightly browned, but not hard.

Calendula petals can be eaten raw in a salad and a tonic tea can be made by adding petals to rosemary, melissa or red clover tea. Use 10 ml (2 tsp) petals to 250 ml (1 cup) boiling water.

Because of the yellow dye in the petals, butter, cream and omelettes can become a beautiful deep yellow colour by adding a few petals to your recipes. Simply boil up the flowers in a little water or butter and add.

Because the calendula flowers have such amazing tonic and healing properties and are of great benefit to the circulatory system, it is said that Arabs feed the plants to their horses, which are world famous for their speed.

The calendula has a mucilaginous agent in its flowers and leaves and it is used in lotions and creams for skin conditions and eczema. It also helps to combat a greasy skin and a skin wash can be made by pouring 1 litre (4 cups) boiling water over 6 calendula flowers. Allow to steep, then strain and use as a wash.

Leaves can be pulped and applied directly to sores and wounds; the poultice cools inflamed parts and cleanses old sores. An eye lotion for treating conjunctivitis can be made by boiling 3 flower-heads in 1 litre (4 cups) water. Bring to the boil for one minute, then strain, cool and use in an eye-bath twice or three times daily.

Seeds can be sown in February for planting out in April. Because of February's heat I have found it best to grow them in seed trays so that the seedlings can be kept moist and shaded. Plant out 30–45 cm apart in well-dug beds with a good dressing of compost. If you keep cutting the flowers for drying, new buds will form and in fact the whole plant benefits from being picked in its flowering season.

CARAWAY

PLATE 6

Family:	*Umbelliferae*
Species:	*Carum carvi*
Plant:	biennial
Height:	60 cm
Soil:	any, good drainage
Exposure:	full sun
Propagation:	seeds
Uses:	culinary

Caraway has a very strong taste – you either love it or really dislike it. In ancient Greece young girls were given caraway to bring colour to pale complexions. The Romans ate the seeds to aid digestion and added caraway seeds to meat dishes to help preserve the meat.

Today caraway seeds are mostly used in cakes and in confectionery but they are also used to flavour pickles, fish, rye bread, Brussels sprouts and cabbage. In fact, cooked with cabbage they not only help the digestion but also clear the air of the cooking smell and give a subtle flavour to an otherwise tasteless vegetable.

Caraway really does not like to be transplanted and I have found it does best sown directly into its site. It needs full sun in a light sandy soil.

Prepare the bed, water well, make shallow drills and sow the seeds about 20 cm apart. Cover with sand and then with a light layer of compost and shade close to the ground with hessian. I tuck the edges of the hessian under stones to keep the hot spring winds from drying out the bed. Keep moist until the seedlings are 5–7 cm high, then harden off by lifting the hessian for 2 hours longer each day until the plants are sturdy.

The seeds can be harvested when ripe and starting to dry. I store them in a brown paper bag until they are bone dry and then transfer them to screw-top glass jars.

Grow caraway as a summer crop only in winter rainfall areas as it dislikes cold, wet conditions.

CASTOR OIL PLANT

PLATE 6

Family: *Euphorbiaceae*
Species: *Ricinus communis*
Plant: perennial shrub
Height: 60 cm – 3 metres
Soil: any
Exposure: full sun
Propagation: seeds
Uses: medicinal

The castor oil plant grows with tremendous ease and abundance and it needs so little attention that it can be placed in an out of the way corner of the garden where it will grow to large proportions. The seeds are poisonous so do warn your children about them, or cut off the flowering head before the seeds form.

The leaves of the castor oil plant are called 'palma Christii' or 'Christ's hands' because of their remarkable healing properties and I feel this plant should be in every herb garden, although it should be cut back to a controllable size.

The leaf is used for treating warts and tumours and as a drawing poultice for wounds and sores. Of course it is also used to make the famous purge but it is a blemish and mole remover too if rubbed onto the affected area daily. The juice from the stem is an effective toothache remedy. The warmed oil is an excellent bruise rub, it removes intestinal worms and, rubbed into the scalp prior to shampooing, helps prevent falling hair and aids hair growth. As a rub for ringworm or mange, take two parts castor oil, one part vinegar, mix together and warm; then rub into the troublesome area night and morning and watch it heal before your eyes.

The seeds can be sprinkled at the entrances of mole burrows and the moles will desert them.

If you suffer from tired and aching feet, warm a leaf or two in hot water, bind them around your feet with a warm towel and rest awhile. Perhaps you should not let your friends see you – but how soothing it feels and how rejuvenating!

In early spring dig the soil over deeply, add a spadeful of compost and plant two or three seeds about 60 cm apart. Cover with leaf mould and water well. Within a week the seeds will push up their heads and grow vigorously all summer. In frost areas they will very likely be cut down but if the root is kept protected they will often send up new leaf shoots in spring.

There is a deep red variety of the castor oil plant with scarlet seed-heads. It is decorative in the garden and the leaves can also be used medicinally. However, it does not have the strength of the wild, old-fashioned *Ricinus communis* which is the valuable medicinal plant. Look along the roadsides, particularly in Natal, and see the abundance with which it grows – should we not be taking a greater interest in this plant which has become almost indigenous?

CATNIP

PLATE 6

Family:	*Labiatae*
Species:	*Nepeta mussinii*, *N. cataria*
Plant:	perennial, hardy
Height:	15–30 cm
Soil:	any
Exposure:	sun, partial shade
Propagation:	cuttings, seeds
Uses:	medicinal, fragrance

Cats love this plant and it is a necessary 'salad' in their diet, so if you have a cat you cannot possibly be without a plant or two. Long ago catnip was used to line herbaceous border walks and the mauvy-blue flowering heads in the greyness of the leaves make a beautiful feature in the garden.

With age the plants can become straggly and should be cut back to keep them neat and compact. *Nepeta cataria* grows up to 60 cm in flowering sprays of white or palest mauve and this is the variety cats find irresistible.

Medicinally, a thumb-sized sprig of catnip and a thumb-sized sprig of marjoram in 125 ml (½ cup) of boiling water, sweetened with a little honey and drunk last thing at night, will help prevent bedwetting. Both herbs have calming, refrigerant and tonic properties.

Catnip can be given to babies with colic, and is excellent for expelling wind and curing hiccoughs in babies and adults. A pain-relieving, nerve-soothing tea can be made with a thumb-length sprig of catnip in 250 ml (1 cup) boiling water, and this is useful, too, for relieving menstrual pain, indigestion and flatulence. A brew can be made using leaf sprays and flowers (15–20 cm) in 1 litre (4 cups) of boiling water. Steep for 2 hours, pour off the water, allow to cool and drink a wineglassful morning and night. For babies, give one teaspoonful before feeds for colic and winds.

Nepeta mussinii makes a beautiful window-box or hanging basket plant as it cascades over the sides of the container. *Mussinii* has the smallest leaves of all the varieties, needs less cutting back and is happy with afternoon shade. *Nepeta cataria* needs full sun and should be cut well back after flowering to the rosette of new leaves at the base.

Save all the clippings to add to sprays for ants and aphids. Even dried leaves sprinkled at ant holes will help deter them.

Cuttings can be taken at any time of the year and should be kept cool and damp until well rooted. (Protect the cutting boxes with wire mesh to prevent cats loving the plants too vigorously!) *Nepeta mussinii* will often branch and send roots into the soil. If clipped away from the mother plant and allowed to establish, these new plants can later be lifted out with a good spadeful of surrounding soil and transplanted. Plant the *Nepeta* varieties 30–45 cm apart and keep trimmed. The trimmed pieces can be dried and used for stuffing into playthings for cats.

Joan van Gogh

1 Angelica _p 19_
2 Anise _p 20_
3 Arum lily _p 21_

1
4
2
3

Joan van Gogh

1 Asparagus *p 22*
2 Basil *p 24*
3 Bay *p 25*
4 Lemon balm (melissa) *p 76*

1 Bergamot *p 26*
2 Borage *p 27*
3 Buttercup *p 29*
4 Calendula *p 30*

2

4

3

1

1 Caraway *p 32*
2 Castor oil *p 33*
3 Catnip *p 34*
4 Celery *p 35*

CELERY

PLATES 6 and 32

Family:	*Umbelliferae*
Species:	*Apium graveolens*
Plant:	biennial
Height:	20–50 cm
Soil:	moist, friable
Exposure:	full sun
Propagation:	seeds
Uses:	culinary, medicinal

One tends to think of celery as a vegetable and not a medicinal herb – but how lucky we are to have the two in one!

Celery soup and celery tea are used to relieve arthritis, rheumatism and neuralgia. Both are effective aids for flatulence. Celery will restore a flagging appetite and is helpful in bringing high blood pressure down to normal.

Five ml (1 tsp) celery seed to 500 ml (2 cups) boiling water, taken once or twice a day, acts as a healthy diuretic and clears sluggish kidneys. Celery seed makes a delicious slimming tea, using one teaspoon seeds to 250 ml (1 cup) boiling water. Steep for 5 minutes and drink as often as you like throughout the day. Use the seeds for flavouring savoury dishes and also in salad dressings.

Celery can be cut and dried; plants which are going into their flowering stage can be pulled up for drying and storing. Always dry in the shade on wire racks or on newspaper and turn the leaves daily. Once they are dry they can be crumbled or chopped up for easier storage and then used in soups and stews or in bouquet garnis.

Seed can be sown in autumn, in boxes under cover or in shallow drills. Cover lightly with fine compost mixed with sand, followed by a light layer of fallen autumn leaves to keep them warm through the winter. You can also sow in spring and cover the seeds with hessian to keep the soil moist. Where the plants come up too thickly, thin out by transplanting – they will take quite easily if they are not too big.

Water well every three days and pile up compost and sand around the base of the plant to assist in blanching the stems. I usually leave half the bed of celery unblanched as the goodness is in the leaves and these are delicious in soups, stews and salads; the blanched stems can be kept for special dishes.

Allow one or two plants to go to seed and collect the seed as soon as it is ripe. Store in airtight bottles. Celery withstands the winter cold so always try to have seedlings at hand to carry through the seasons.

CHAMOMILE

PLATE 7

Family:	*Compositae*
Species:	*Matricaria recutita*
Plant:	perennial
Height:	up to 30 cm
Soil:	light
Exposure:	partial shade
Propagation:	cuttings, seeds
Uses:	medicinal, cosmetic

There are several varieties of chamomile and it seems as if many small-flowered, white daisy-like plants have been given that name. The leaves of the true chamomile are fine and delicate, hair-like and minutely divided, and have a faintly aromatic smell. The flowers consist of yellow and white ligulate florets 15 mm – 3 mm wide, borne singly on long erect stems. They are indigenous to Europe where they have been used for centuries in healing medicines.

Chamomile's medicinal uses are many and varied: anti-inflammatory, antiseptic, antispasmodic, carminative, soothing for coughs, colds, gastric disorders and, in large doses, it is also emetic. The standard brew is 250 ml (1 cup) leaves and blossoms to 570 ml (1 pint) boiling water. Stand and then strain and take 125 ml (½ cup) three times a day. A weak infusion acts as a tonic and as a cleansing douche. It can be used as a wash for ulcers, a gargle for mouth ulcers and it is known to be popular and effective in France and Spain as a soothing medicine for children. Its tonic, soothing and calming properties for infants are acknowledged by the orthodox medical profession. When used as a rinse it will bring out the highlights in fair hair and it is also an excellent eye lotion.

Chamomile tea is easily made: steep a dessertspoon of dried or fresh blossoms in boiling water, strain and sweeten with honey. It is a wonderful bedtime drink.

Propagate by sowing seeds in sand-filled trays, pressing down well and covering with a fine layer of sand. Keep fairly moist until the seedlings are big enough to handle. Plant out into well-dug, well-composted, light soil, in partial shade, about 20 cm apart, and keep well watered. Chamomile needs coolness and moisture to do well. Pick the flowers for using in pot-pourris or cut them for small posies; you will find they last well in water.

CHERVIL

Family:	*Umbelliferae*
Species:	*Anthriscus cerefolium*
Plant:	annual
Height:	30–46 cm
Soil:	average, moist
Exposure:	shade
Propagation:	seeds
Uses:	culinary
Meaning:	sincerity

Chervil is a dainty cooling herb and is not as difficult to grow as was once thought. The secret is that chervil needs shade, particularly against our harsh South African sun. Grown in moist, well-composted soil under vines or fruit trees, where only a bit of early morning sun reaches it, chervil will do very well.

Chervil is one of the ingredients in *herbes fines* and is a delicious addition to sauces and salads. Related to parsley, it can in fact be used in place of parsley but it must be introduced to the dish only at the last moment or it will lose its goodness and flavour.

For a constant supply sow the seed where it is to mature, cover lightly with compost and keep moist. There is no need to cover with hessian if it is shaded by vines or trees. I sow a new row when the first row appears above the soil. This way, all through summer you will be sure of a good supply. Cut the plants to the ground when you pick for salads, as this encourages new leaves to be produced. As a general guide the plants are usually ready for cutting 6–8 weeks after sowing. Transplant when just big enough to handle or thin out, leaving 20 cm space between plants. One or two pots could be sown in the last week of February for winter use on the kitchen window-sill.

CHICORY

PLATE 7

Family:	*Compositae*
Species:	*Cichorium intybus*
Plant:	perennial
Height:	up to 120 cm
Soil:	rich, well-drained
Exposure:	sun
Propagation:	seeds
Uses:	culinary, medicinal
Meaning:	frugality

Chicory has long had a reputation as a medicinal herb. The beautiful blue flowers were once distilled to make a soothing eye-wash and they were also candied, as were violet blossoms, for use as cake decorations.

There is a wild variety which has serrated leaves and eye-catching bright blue flowers and it can be found growing along the roadside, and there are the cultivated varieties as well, of which perhaps the most well known is 'witloof'.

The whole plant is an important tonic herb and, bitter tasting though it is, it is quite edible. The tap root can be roasted and ground and made into a coffee substitute. The root can also be boiled and eaten and, as it is such a valuable nerve and digestive tonic, it should be included in salads. The young green leaves are edible, too, as are the flowers. The older leaves should be lightly boiled before eating (throw off the first water and then boil up again to remove some of the bitterness). A tea can be made from the leaves and flowers – 125 ml (½ cup) leaves and flowers to 500 ml (2 cups) boiling water. A small wineglassful three times a day will bring about improvement in cases of jaundice, anaemia, weak sight, infertility and all liver disorders.

Chicory likes soil that is deep and rich so prepare a bed well and dig in a lavish amount of compost and old manure, for it is in the tap root, which is long and vigorous, that most of its wonderful medicinal properties are found.

Sow seed in sand trays and cover with a piece of glass until the seedlings are strong. Keep well watered at all times. Plant out into a well-prepared bed 30 cm apart and keep shaded for a day or two. To blanch, tie the outer leaves together over the crown and heap the soil up around them several weeks before harvesting. If the plants get wet after heavy rain or watering open up the leaves and dry them off before tying them up again. In very hot weather the plant runs to seed so it is best to sow seeds in March for winter planting out.

CHIVES

PLATE 7

Family:	*Liliaceae*
Species:	*Allium schoenoprasum*, *A. tuberosum*
Plant:	perennial
Height:	15–30 cm
Soil:	fairly rich
Exposure:	sun, can take partial shade
Propagation:	division, seed
Uses:	culinary, medicinal

A precious culinary herb, chives are so easy to grow, in beds or in pots, that no one need be without a clump or two. Another *Allium* species closely related to *A. schoenoprasum* is *Allium tuberosum*, the garlic chive, which is powerfully strong in flavour but not as prolific in growth.

Chives' round, mauvy-pink flowering heads appear in spring and summer and can be used in salads, while the more mature flowers can be made into a delicious vinegar called Chive Blossom Vinegar.

CHIVE BLOSSOM VINEGAR

Fill a glass jar with chive blossoms and fill to the top with white vinegar. Cork and set in the sun for ten days. Strain the now pink liquid and, if a stronger flavour or colour is desired, repack the bottle with fresh blossoms and allow to stand for a further ten days. Fill a bottle with the strained vinegar; a few fresh flower-heads and leaves, tied together, can be put into the top of the bottle for decoration and identification. Use in salad dressings and in fish sauces.

Chives can be cut back and chopped into small pieces for drying to flavour soups and stews or for using in *bouquet garnis*, but they are really nicer used fresh.

Chives are blood-cleansing, improve the appetite and act as a general tonic for the whole body.

Seeds can be sown in trays at any time of the year except May, June and July. They must be kept under glass until the seedlings are a centimetre or two high and then hardened off by exposing to a little sun each day. It is important to keep the box moist so take care not to let it dry out. Plant out 20 cm apart when big enough to handle. Clumps will form and will stay healthy for 4–5 years; they can then be taken up and redivided. Leaves will start to die down in the midsummer heat and in midwinter but if you dig in compost they will send up vigorous new growth. Do not cut all the leaves from a plant or they will lose their means of food manufacture. Instead, cut off the outer leaves at the base, and grow a good row of chives for constant picking.

Garlic chives are unfussy in any garden and their seeds, too, germinate well.

Grow in seed beds or boxes, keep damp and plant out at least 30 cm apart when the little plants are big enough to handle. They have an attractive white flower in green bracts and a delicious garlic flavoured vinegar can be made by using the flowering heads in the same way as in making chive blossom vinegar. Add a few leaves for the first ten days to impart a strong flavour.

COLUMBINE

PLATE 8

Family:	*Ranunculaceae*
Species:	*Aquilegia vulgaris* (granny's bonnet)
Plant:	perennial
Height:	up to 60 cm
Soil:	rich, well-drained
Exposure:	partial shade
Propagation:	seeds, division
Uses:	medicinal, landscape
Meaning:	folly

The columbine is named from the Latin *columba*, meaning 'dove', a reference to the shape of the flower's curved spurs. In the Middle Ages it was known as 'aquilinae', from the Latin *aquila*, meaning 'eagle', likening the shape of the flower's spurs to bird of prey's claws.

It was used medicinally in the seventeenth century as an anti-scorbutic and as a remedy for hysteria and sleeplessness. It is still used in homoeopathic medicine today for menstrual problems, insomnia and nervousness. *The plant is poisonous, however, so use it only under the guidance of a homoeopathic doctor.* The roots, leaves and flowers all have antiseptic, astringent and sedative properties but only the root may be used externally, and this for the treatment of ulcers. *The seed is extremely poisonous and may be fatal if swallowed by a child.*

Sow the seeds in trays of sand and keep moist and protected by covering with a sheet of glass until they germinate. Keep the seedlings shaded and well watered until they are strong enough to handle. Plant in partial shade in well-dug, rich soil to which several spadefuls of compost have been added (3–4 spadefuls to 1 square metre). Keep well watered until they are established. Thereafter water twice a week and separate in spring if the clump becomes too large. Each spring a spadeful of compost can be dug in around each plant.

There are several varieties of columbine, many of which are hybrids. Most of them have medicinal properties but all are poisonous so do take care.

COMFREY

PLATE 8

Family:	*Boraginaceae*
Species:	*Symphytum officinale*
Plant:	perennial, dies down in winter in cold areas
Height:	30–45 cm
Soil:	average, loves moisture
Exposure:	sun, partial shade
Propagation:	division, pieces of root
Uses:	medicinal, culinary

Comfrey's other name is 'knit-bone', a reference to its capacity to generate the healing of broken bones. In fact comfrey is useful in the treating of all manner of ailments, including ulcers, tuberculosis, pneumonia, ruptures, burns and bruises.

For healing bruises, swellings, sprains and strains a comfrey poultice is a wonder worker. Chop 3 or 4 comfrey leaves finely, soften in a little hot water and apply to the area on a square of lint. Cover with a piece of plastic and bandage in place. It also brings relief to rheumatism and arthritis sufferers. Fresh leaves rubbed onto the skin will repel insects and soothe bites and stings.

The young leaves can be chopped finely and used in salads or soups and stews and chopped, uncooked comfrey leaves added to mashed potato makes an appetising dish.

In colder areas leaves can also be dried on wire racks for winter use, then packed into glass bottles and corked to keep them dust free.

Comfrey generally does well throughout South Africa but it does love water so in times of drought it will struggle to survive.

The plant can be divided and even pieces of root will quickly grow into vigorous plants if kept moist. It does best in deeply manured soil and comfrey plantings will often solve the problem of badly drained ground. It will also thrive on the edge of swamp ground where it will make a lush border.

On the compost heap comfrey is a valuable asset, breaking down quickly and easily. Do not throw away even one leaf for comfrey adds nourishing minerals to the compost.

CORIANDER

PLATE 8

Family:	*Umbelliferae*
Species:	*Coriandrum sativum*
Plant:	annual
Height:	30–60 cm
Soil:	light, moderately rich
Exposure:	sun
Propagation:	seeds
Uses:	culinary, pot-pourris
Meaning:	hidden worth

Coriander is one of the prettiest members of the *Umbelliferae* family. It has fine skeleton leaves and clusters of soft mauve flowers. Its seed heads, too, are attractive, particularly in dried flower arrangements.

Coriander's history goes back a long way. It was found in early Egyptian tombs and is referred to in the Bible as a comparison to manna. The Romans used it with caraway to preserve meat.

Coriander is an ingredient in commercially sold mixed spice and a delicious home-mixed flavouring can be made by crushing and powdering equal quantities of cinnamon, coriander, nutmeg and a half quantity of cloves. Mix well and use wherever a recipe calls for mixed spice.

In some market stalls, particularly Indian markets and some oriental shops, you may come across bunches of fresh leaves for sale labelled 'Chinese parsley' or 'cilantro'. These are none other than coriander leaves and are used in oriental cooking and in salads. Coriander is related to parsley and is delicious in salads as a dressing.

CORIANDER SALAD DRESSING

125 ml (½ cup) Cardin oil or maize or sunflower oil
125 ml (½ cup) freshly squeezed lemon juice
10 ml (1 dessertsp) honey
20 ml (2 dessertsp) coriander leaves, chopped
10 ml (2 tsp) thyme
10 ml (2 tsp) sage, finely chopped

Mix together oil, lemon juice and honey by shaking in a screw-top bottle. Add chopped coriander leaves, and the thyme and chopped sage. Pour over a mixed salad just before serving.

If you want to use the leaves as a garnish and in salads coriander will do well in a container on a stoep or patio in the sun. It does become straggly as a container plant, however, if you wait for the seed heads to dry.

It is best to sow seeds in spring in light, well-tilled soil in the place where they are to grow. Make a shallow drill and sow the seeds 15–20 cm apart. Cover with sand

and a layer of compost to retain the moisture. Cover with hessian and keep damp until the seeds are well established. Then harden off by exposing to full sunlight, initially for two hours, increasing by two-hourly periods daily until the seedlings are able to withstand the heat and sun.

Seeds can be sown every fortnight and this will ensure a continuous crop. Mature seeds can be used in pot-pourris as they act as a fixative. In fact there are so many uses for the seeds – flavouring stews, sausages, salads, beans, pastries and even wines – that it is a most rewarding plant to grow in a corner of the vegetable garden.

CORNFLOWER

PLATE 8

Family: *Compositae*
Species: *Centaurea cyanus*
Plant: annual
Height: 30–90 cm
Soil: average
Exposure: sun
Propagation: seeds
Uses: medicinal

In midsummer the glorious royal blue cornflower quite lifts the spirits, making even one bush a worthwhile addition to the garden. Not only pleasing to the eye, the cornflower has wonderful medicinal properties too. An uplifting tonic tea, which aids digestion and nervousness, can be made by pouring 250 ml (1 cup) boiling water over 5 flowers. Add honey as a sweetener, a slice of lemon for flavour, and sip just before going to sleep.

An eyewash can also be made from the flowers and this is an effective treatment for chronic and acute eye inflammations, as well as for corneal ulcers. Pour 1 litre (4 cups) boiling water over 50 flower-heads and allow to stand for half an hour. Strain through muslin, and bathe the eyes three times a day. This same brew washes out and cleans cuts and grazes. Flowers can be added to pot-pourris for colour and a blue dye can also be made by boiling flowers in water and leaving to stand overnight.

Sow the fly-away seeds in shallow trays of wet sand. Cover with just enough sand to hold them down and water from underneath by standing the tray in a pan of water for a while each day until the seeds germinate. They can then be lightly sprayed with water from above. Plant out when the seedlings are big enough to handle. Seeds sown in trays in August are usually ready to plant out in mid September. Space them 30–45 cm apart in well-dug soil to which a generous dressing of compost has been added.

The seeds and young plants are not fussy and need only to be kept moist. They grow into tall, upright bushes and the more often you cut the flowers the more buds will be produced. I pick bunches for the kitchen table and then use the flowers as they fade to dry for pot-pourris.

Once they are established in the garden cornflowers will self-seed and each spring the green rosette of leaves will pop up in all sorts of surprising places. I have transplanted cornflowers quite successfully to ensure that they are displayed to their best advantage. Do make sure that a good spadeful of soil is dug up with the plant when you do so however. They need no further attention except for a weekly watering. Re-sow annually.

COTTON LAVENDER (SANTOLINA)

PLATE 25

Family: *Compositae*
Species: *Santolina chamaecyparissus*
Plant: perennial
Height: up to 60 cm
Soil: average
Exposure: sun
Propagation: cuttings
Uses: landscape, insecticide

Santolina can be clipped into an attractive low hedge and it can be used effectively in formal gardens and in knot gardens. It was once used as an antispasmodic medicine but it has a very bitter taste and eventually lost its popularity. It is now rarely used medicinally. The flowers dry well and remain strong and sturdy. As soon as the flowers are mature pick and tie them in bunches and hang them upside down to dry.

Bruised santolina sprigs placed between the pages of books will help combat fish-moths and if they are replaced regularly with fresh sprigs the fish-moths will soon disappear altogether. Santolina is also a valued ingredient in moth-repelling sachets.

MOTH REPELLENT SACHETS

Equal quantities of:
santolina
southernwood
rue
wormwood
lavender

To this mixture add one part crushed lemon and naartjie peel and a sprinkling of cloves. Add a few drops of lavender oil. Stand sealed for ten days, shaking daily, then fill sachets with this mixture and place behind books and in record holders. Revive from time to time with a few drops of lavender oil and a few freshly dried sprigs of santolina. Make the sachets fairly flat so that they can be packed between books and files.

Take cuttings by pulling off strong side shoots with a small heel and root in trays of wet sand. Spring cuttings are the quickest to root but cuttings can be taken at any time of the year except in the coldest months. Plant out 60 cm apart when well rooted and clip during summer to keep tailored.

COTYLEDON

PLATE 21

Family: *Crassulaceae*
Species: *Cotyledon orbiculata* (pig's ear)
Plant: perennial
Height: up to 60 cm
Soil: dry
Exposure: full sun
Propagation: leaf, cuttings
Uses: medicinal

In many South African gardens the cotyledon can be found and there are a number of varieties. *Cotyledon orbiculata* or pig's ear, with the red margin and slightly sticky surface to the leaf, is the well-used one. It can be applied locally to plantar and other warts by scratching the surface of the leaf and applying the juicy area to the wart; hold in position with sticking plaster. Replace daily with a fresh piece of leaf, for 10 days or until the wart drops off.

Many varieties of crassula and cotyledon are used by African people as a drawing poultice, for earache (a warmed leaf held next to the ear or warmed leaf juice drops in the ear) and for toothache. Care should be taken in identifying the correct variety, however, as several are poisonous. This applies to any plant used medicinally. Never use a plant that you are not certain of.

Propagation is simple – merely break off a piece of the existing plant and press it into moist soil. Keep moist for a few days and new roots will quickly establish it. Even a leaf generates a growing plant and often a fallen leaf will make a tiny new plant, feeding off the leaf. This can be planted by merely covering the leaf with soil and leaving the new plant uncovered and firmly placed.

The pig's ear plants do not demand rich soil and do well in drought and harsh conditions. They do need some protection from heavy frost, however, as they are frost tender. I find that a few handfuls of veld grass tucked over them are enough protection to winter them well.

Plant out new cuttings directly into their permanent site 45 cm apart. Water in the first two or three weeks; thereafter they only need sporadic watering. They do well with an occasional spadeful of compost forked in around them. They grow very straggly in shade so choose a place in full sun for them as these are typical South African sun lovers.

CRAB APPLE

PLATE 9

Family:	*Rosaceae*
Species:	*Malus floribunda, M. hupehensis*
Plant:	small shrub
Height:	1–3 m
Soil:	average, well-drained
Exposure:	sun
Propagation:	seed
Uses:	culinary, decorative, medicinal

Every herb garden needs an old-fashioned crab apple, which comes from the same family as the domestic apple. Once long ago it was used to make a potent and magical drink called verjuice, and under its influence it was believed that you would see fairies!

Crab apple is tonic, cleansing and anti-scabies, and it is also a wonderful cure for most stomach disorders. Dosage is 125 ml (½ cup) grated or chopped fruit, scalded with 100 ml hot (not boiling) water, sweetened with honey and taken three times a day.

A delicious jelly can also be made from the midsummer fruits, first allowing the little apples to mature on the tree before picking.

CRAB APPLE JELLY

2 kg (4 lb) crab apples
1–1,7 litres (2–3 pts) cold water
rind of 2 lemons
sugar

Wash apples and remove any blemishes. Do not peel or core. Quarter and place in a large saucepan together with lemon rind. Pour in enough cold water to cover the apples and lemon rind and simmer for one hour until the apples are soft and mushy. Pour into a large cloth suspended over a basin and drain overnight. Measure the amount of juice and pour back into the pot. Add 450 g (1 lb) sugar to every 600 ml (1 pt) juice. Place the pot over a low heat and stir to dissolve the sugar. Bring to the boil and skim off any scum that rises to the surface. Boil for approximately 10 minutes or until setting point is reached. Remove from stove and cool. Pour into hot jars, cover with pieces of grease-proof paper soaked in vinegar and screw on tops. Store in a cool pantry.

The crab apple shrub should be planted in well-composted soil, spaced 2 m apart. Dig a hole and fill with water, topsoil and compost and allow it to stand overnight before planting. It is a slow grower and can be started from seed. Nurseries offer several varieties but choose the old-fashioned white or pink flowered, non-hybridised crab apple.

DILL

Family:	*Umbelliferae*
Species:	*Peucedanum graveolens*
Plant:	annual
Height:	90–120 cm
Soil:	average, well-drained
Exposure:	full sun
Propagation:	seeds
Uses:	culinary
Meaning:	protection

Dill was once used as a magic herb by sorcerers and magicians in their spell-casting and it was believed that branches of dill hung above a front door would protect the house from witchcraft.

Dill is not as easy to grow as its first cousin fennel and they should be kept far apart in the herb garden as they cross pollinate. Dill does not grow as prolifically as fennel either but it is worth persisting as it is such a delicious flavouring for fish dishes; of course the seeds are also used in pickling and medicinally to aid digestion. It is distinguished from fennel by its more fragile, finer and greyer leaf plumes.

Keep dill seeds in a sealed jar on the bathroom shelf and chew a few for flatulence or heartburn and indigestion whenever the need arises.

Sow dill each spring and again in January as it goes quickly to seed and loses flavour. Seed can be sown in egg boxes, or in jiffy pots. The whole box can be put into the ground and the cardboard allowed to disintegrate. Alternatively seed can be sown in the ground straight away and kept moist and covered until the seedlings appear. Harden off by removing the shade cloth for longer periods each day and always keep fairly moist. Dill has a tap root and therefore does not transplant easily.

A spadeful of compost should be forked in lightly around the maturing plants. If you cut away the flowering stalks as soon as the first buds appear, you will have your dill plant for several seasons.

ELDER

PLATE 9

Family:	*Caprifoliaceae*
Species:	*Sambucus nigra*
Plant:	perennial shrub
Height:	90 cm – 3,6 m
Soil:	not fussy
Exposure:	sun
Propagation:	runners, cuttings
Uses:	medicinal, culinary
Meaning:	zealousness

Elder trees are essential in herb gardens (or in any garden for that matter) as they keep witches away! Elder is one of the most versatile of herbs and was a particular favourite of the Greek physician Hippocrates, the Father of Medicine. All parts of the plant have their uses and so, as it also grows with such ease, no garden dare be without it.

The dried root of the elder, pounded, then simmered in water for several minutes, is used as a treatment for kidney and lymphatic ailments. The bark is used in treating epilepsy in the following way: dry the inner bark of old branches and stems and steep 12,5 ml (1 tbls) in a small glass of red or white wine. A dose taken nightly in the epileptic's quiet periods is beneficial and when the onset of a fit is expected a wine-glass can be taken every 20 minutes.

Elder leaves can be boiled into insect-repelling lotion which is highly effective when wiped over the skin. Take 6 cups elder leaves, well pressed down, and pour over 1 litre (4 cups) boiling water. Steep for 10 minutes, strain and use. Mixed with 250 ml (1 cup) scented geranium leaves and 250 ml (1 cup) chopped garlic cloves, the brew also makes a potent remedy for ringworm, itchiness and scrofula. A plain leaf brew is a wonderful cure for eczema. The flowers are used in treatments for coughs, colds, sore throats, eye ailments, burns, scalds and erysipelas sores. Boil 6 flower-heads in 1 litre (4 cups) water, strain and cool and apply on cotton-wool to the affected area. For colds and throat infections, use the same brew as a gargle, and for eye problems as an eye-bath.

The berries, too, are useful in soothing coughs and sore throats. They should first be pounded in honey. Taken as a daily dose, the mixture is also helpful in treating anaemia and, both externally and internally, it can be used for treating malignant skin growths (using equal quantities of berries and honey). As a burn dressing the juice of the ripe berries will give instant relief and can be applied often to soothe the affected area.

There are many elder recipes, all of which are health-giving and delicious. I make elder flower cakes as a quick and easy treat for visitors who come to see the herb garden.

1
2
3
4

1 Chamomile *p 36*
2 Chervil *p 37*
3 Chicory *p 38*
4 Chives *p 39*

8

1 Columbine *p 41*
2 Comfrey *p 42*
3 Coriander *p 43*
4 Cornflower *p 45*

1
2
3

1 Crab apple *p 48*
2 Dill *p 49*
3 Elder *p 50*

1 Fennel *p 52*
2 Feverfew *p 53*
3 Foxglove *p 54*

ELDER FLOWER CAKES

160 ml (⅔ cup) milk
20 g (2 tbls) butter
2 eggs
190 ml (¾ cup) sugar
250 ml (1 cup) elder flowers
250 ml (1 cup) flour
10 ml (2 tsp) baking powder
5 ml (1 tsp) vanilla

Boil together milk and butter. Beat up eggs and sugar. Mix together elder flowers, flour, baking powder and vanilla. Add the flour mixture to the beaten sugar and eggs alternately with the boiled milk and butter, a little at a time, all the while whisking well.

Pour into individual, well-greased muffin-type pans. Bake at 200°C (400°F) for about 10 minutes or until lightly browned. Cool slightly, then cut off tops and place a teaspoon of whipped cream on top of each cake. Slice the cut-off top of the little cake in half and press it into the cream to look like butterfly wings. Dust with icing sugar and serve on a plate decorated with fresh elder flowers and leaves.

When planting elder trees I have found that the only way to check the invading roots which all send up vigorous small trees is to line a large deep hole with thick plastic. Do not put plastic into the bottom of the hole, however, only around the sides. Fill with topsoil and compost and then plant the tree; firm well and keep watered until new growth is started. Thereafter the elder is unfussy, withstanding drought, but benefiting from a deep weekly watering.

The elder is deciduous and in areas prone to frost may be neatly trimmed back in the winter. The cut branches can be trimmed further and pushed into wet sand to start up new trees. It does in fact become straggly if it is not kept trimmed and the root shoots chopped out. A hedge of elders at the back of the herb garden makes a beautiful back-drop and if planted on the western side provides shade for the summer afternoons. Do remember to edge the furrow (about 45 cm deep) with plastic to prevent the runners invading. Space the trees 1,5 metres apart. Pieces of rooted runners can be transplanted before the top growth is too tall. Trim and keep watered until new shoots appear. Thereafter water well once a week.

Each spring a spadeful of compost can be dug in around the base of the elder and a mulch of leaves in winter will keep the roots warm. Other than the occasional trimming, elder is undemanding and an asset in all gardens – a veritable apothecary shop close at hand.

FENNEL

PLATES 10 and 32

Family:	*Umbelliferae*
Species:	*Foeniculum vulgare*, F. var *dulce*
Plant:	perennial
Height:	up to 1,5 m; 60 cm
Soil:	light, well-drained
Exposure:	full sun
Propagation:	seeds
Uses:	culinary, medicinal
Meaning:	worthy of praise

Fennel is a very easy plant to grow, but do pay attention to where you place it as it is a bad companion to certain plants (see section on companion planting).

Foeniculum vulgare is mostly used for flavouring, while Florence fennel, *Foeniculum* var *dulce*, is a delicious vegetable, much loved in Italy, where it is known as 'finocchio'. When using the latter, harvest the bulb before the plant flowers. The bulb can be boiled and served topped with a rich cheese sauce, browned under the grill just before serving. It can also be finely shaved into salads.

The finely chopped leaves are delicious in fish dishes and on green beans.

Young stems of *Foeniculum vulgare* can be chopped into salads and they can also be cooked like asparagus and served with a vinegar and butter dressing, but first cut the stems before the flowers open. Chopped leaves in cream cheese, sprinkled with lemon pepper makes a delicious dip for savoury biscuits or sticks of celery.

Fennel is a wonderful digestive herb. A piece of stem or leaf can be chewed after a hearty meal to combat indigestion and that 'too full' feeling.

A brew for slimmers can be made by boiling 250 ml (1 cup) chopped fennel leaves and stalk in 750 ml (3 cups) water for 6–10 minutes, keeping the pot covered. Allow to cool and then drink at intervals throughout the day.

Use fennel water in soups and stews. Make it fresh daily and it will tone and aid weight loss.

Fennel seeds itself readily and transplants fairly easily if it is still small. It usually needs full sun and well-drained soil, although I have grown it on turf and it has done very well there too. Plant seedlings 50–60 cm apart and keep moist for a few weeks until established.

Start fennel plants with seeds and keep moist until they are a fairly good size and then leave them to themselves. When the plants die down save some of the stems to use when grilling fish: lay the fish on top of the stems and the fragrance and flavour will permeate the fish. Discard when cooked.

Fennel seeds are a useful fixative in pot-pourris. Crush and mix them with powdered cinnamon and nutmeg.

52

FEVERFEW

PLATE 10

Family:	*Compositae*
Species:	*Chrysanthemum parthenium*
Plant:	perennial, biennial
Height:	30–90 cm
Soil:	well-drained
Exposure:	sun, partial shade
Propagation:	seeds, cuttings
Uses:	medicinal, pot-pourris, landscape
Meaning:	young love

Feverfew is a delightful asset in the garden as it is both an attractive cut flower and an insect repellent. The dried flowers can be used in pot-pourris as they do not break too easily.

Long ago it was believed that a wreath of feverfew leaves bound around the head would soothe a headache. In fact it is now coming into fashion again and migraine and arthritis sufferers find that a brew made of 3 leaves to 250 ml (1 cup) boiling water is most effective in relieving pain. Young leaves eaten in a salad will also help cure a migraine. Three leaves taken daily for 1 month is the most usual dosage.

Feverfew is a famous 'woman's' herb, used as a tonic and general remedy for problems to do with miscarriages, labour pains and infertility. The whole herb, crushed to a pulp, also makes a soothing poultice and is a comforting suppository for painful piles.

Seeds germinate well, sown in boxes of river sand. Keep shaded and damp under a pane of glass until the seedlings are up. Then keep watered until they can be hardened off by exposing them to sunlight for periods of increasing length each day. Plant out 30 cm apart in well-dug and composted soil. If the flowering head is allowed to set seed the plant will not remain perennial, so cut and enjoy the flowers in vases. With tansy leaves and flowers, feverfew can be made into an insect-repellent posy and the dried flowers used in pot-pourris will keep insects out of the mixtures.

For cuttings, pull off lower small branches with a small 'heel' and insert into sand, keeping moist until they root.

Be sure of identifying feverfew correctly as it has several close relatives. The lime green-leafed matricaria is easily confused with feverfew, as are the chamomiles. Feverfew's leaves are a darker green and more finely formed than the other varieties. Several nurseries unwittingly sell matricaria as feverfew so do check carefully.

FOXGLOVE

PLATE 10

Family: *Scrophulariaceae*
Species: *Digitalis purpurea*
Plant: biennial
Height: up to 120 cm
Soil: rich, acid
Exposure: partial shade
Propagation: seeds
Uses: medicinal
Meaning: insincerity

Indigenous to Western Europe, the foxglove prefers an acid soil in partial shade. In most parts of South Africa the hot sun tends to burn it but if the roots are kept cool it will do well anywhere. There are many garden varieties of digitalis but it is the old-fashioned mauve variety, *Digitalis purpurea*, that gives foxglove its place in international medicine.

Digitalis is a popular drug prepared from dried foxglove leaves and used as a heart stimulant in orthodox medicine. As there are poisonous properties in the foxglove, it should only be taken internally under a doctor's supervision. The plant is also an external remedy for the leaves are sedative and, if warmed in hot water and bound over the afflicted area, will ease pain and reduce swellings of all kinds, including tumours. Held in place on the forehead, they will also relieve a headache, while a piece of leaf, rolled and warmed, is soothing for earache. Place it in the ear and hold a hotwater bottle against it for a short while.

A lotion can be made to wash out sore, tired eyes: take 3 or 4 leaves, heat in 600 ml (1 pt) water to just below boiling point, remove the leaves and use as a lotion. The same lotion will help to fade freckles; dab onto the freckles daily or use as a wash.

Whenever using foxgloves it is important to do so only under the supervision of a homoeopathic doctor or qualified herbalist as the plant is poisonous.

Sow seeds in late spring in sand and keep the seed tray moist and protected. A pane of glass over the tray will help maintain the even temperature and moisture. Prick out when the seedlings are big enough to handle and plant 50 cm apart in a well-dug bed which has a liberal amount of compost worked into it – 3–4 spadefuls per square metre. Keep well watered in the first few weeks until the plants establish themselves; thereafter a twice weekly watering will ensure lush growth. Foxgloves usually flower in their second year and I have found that cutting the flowering spike just as it reaches its full beauty gives another year to the life of the plant. The following year a new spike will present itself.

The flowers last well in water if they are first put into a vase of boiling water for about 10 minutes and then into a deep container of cold water. Including a few leaves in your arrangement will prolong the life of the flowers.

GARDEN VALERIAN

Family:	*Valerianaceae*
Species:	*Centranthus ruber* (red valerian)
Plant:	perennial
Height:	20–60 cm
Soil:	average, preferably well-drained
Exposure:	sun
Propagation:	root division
Uses:	medicinal, culinary
Meaning:	accommodating

Red valerian is one of those old-fashioned plants that has given up its place in the garden to more spectacular flowers. Perhaps it deserves another look, however, for not only was it once used medicinally, for ague and dropsy, but its root and leaves are also edible. There are red, pink and white valerian varieties and they make a charming addition to any garden. They are attractive as cut flowers and last well in the vase if a little sugar is added to the water.

Valerian leaves can be cooked to make a spinach. Boil up in water, remove the leaves and throw the water out (this will get rid of the bitterness). Boil up in fresh water to which lemon juice has been added (1 lemon to a medium pot of leaves). Drain well, add salt and pepper to taste and a lump of butter. Chopped leaves and roots can also be added to soup.

Valerian is a tonic herb and is good for blood cleansing. Because of its bitter taste, however, it is not often used.

Valerian is propagated by root division and cuttings. Prepare a bed of well-dug soil in a sunny spot of the garden and add several spades of compost. Plant out 45–60 cm apart and keep moist for a day or two until it is established. Once it is established in a rich, well-dug soil red valerian needs no further attention for at least two years other than a weekly watering. Every two years in spring or autumn clumps can be separated and planted out into freshly dug and composted ground. Keep the flower-heads cut back as soon as they fade.

Garden valerian should not be confused with the medicinal valerian, *Valeriana officinalis*. This was the ancient herb used by the Arab physicians in the tenth century and a tincture of *V. officinalis* was used in the First World War to treat shellshock. Even today the rhizome and roots are still listed in several national pharmacopoeias. Its medicinal uses are sedative, antispasmodic, carminative and calming in a wide range of nervous disorders. It is often combined with other remedies for the treatment of hypertension and it is also useful in treating insomnia, migraine, nervous exhaustion, anxiety and tension. It is a valuable herb in homoeopathy and herbalism but it should be used with caution when treating oneself for overdoses are dangerous. You would be wise, therefore, to use valeriana only under the supervision of a doctor or trained herbalist.

With regard to growing conditions, valeriana is relatively undemanding. It likes a little shade and fairly well-drained soil. It is an unusual plant in South Africa and not at all easy to find, and even when one has it in the herb garden its rather unobtrusive pale pink or white end of summer flowers tend to be overlooked. It will not tolerate heat or drought so be careful where you place it. Divide up the clump every 2 or 3 years in the autumn and plant out 60 cm apart.

Once the flowers are spent cut back the tall flowering stalk and dry the flowers and leaves for a pot-pourri for they retain a fresh fragrance. Roots or rhizomes should be planted 60 cm apart in well-composted soil. I find that the plants wilt in the heat of midsummer so try to plant them where they will have shade from midday onwards. They will need a good watering twice a week and as they are perennials they can be lifted and divided in July or early August and replanted.

Valeriana's natural habitat in Europe and West Asia is along the edges of streams and in damp meadows, so if you are lucky enough to have a plant make sure to keep it cool and damp.

GARLIC

PLATE 11

Family:	*Liliaceae*
Species:	*Allium sativum*
Plant:	annual
Height:	up to 60 cm
Soil:	light, well-drained
Exposure:	sun
Propagation:	seeds, bulblets or cloves
Uses:	culinary, medicinal

Garlic has been cultivated for centuries from Asia to the Mediterranean and has never lost its popularity. Easy to grow, it is an undemanding plant and takes up only a little space for an entire medicine chest of goodness.

Garlic is one of the few herbs that is beneficial for almost any disorder of the human body. When the body is in normal health it is useful as a tonic, antiseptic and a worm deterrent. It gives protection against all kinds of infections, expels toxic elements and is a wonderful aid for bringing down a fever. It is particularly beneficial for disorders of the lungs, including tuberculosis, for which it is a specific. It is also helpful in treating high blood pressure, obesity, arthritis, rheumatism and sciatica.

It is preferable to eat garlic raw (chew a sprig of parsley, thyme or mint afterwards to cleanse the breath). A good dose is a handful of leaves and 2 or 3 cloves, chopped, to equal half a cup. Add to your daily salad or spread on bread mixed with mayonnaise. Garlic can of course be cooked into many dishes and in this way it supplies its food value and flavouring and its own beneficial oil. Medicinally, however, it is only valuable taken raw.

Plant individual cloves broken off from the main bulb in well-dug soil to which a spadeful or two of well-rotted manure has been added and thoroughly dug into the soil. Space the cloves 15 cm apart and 5 cm deep. Keep moist until they shoot. Thereafter water well every few days if you want rich, succulent garlic bulbs. They will also benefit from a leaf mulch to keep the soil cool, moist and friable.

Seed can be sown in seed trays of sand in spring or in autumn. Keep moist and protected until well up, then harden off by placing in the sun for longer periods of time each day. Do not allow to dry out. Plant 15 cm apart when big enough to handle. Allow the bulbs to mature and the top growth to dry and die down before reaping. Cease watering once the leaves start to turn yellow and the flower appears. The bulbs will dry well and retain their wonderful medicinal properties for several months.

GERMANDER

PLATE 12

Family:	*Labiatae*
Species:	*Teucrium chamaedrys*
Plant:	perennial
Height:	30–60 cm
Soil:	unfussy
Exposure:	sun, partial shade
Propagation:	cuttings, seed
Uses:	medicinal, landscape
Meaning:	facility

The germanders are a wide and varying species. *Teucrium chamaedrys* is the low-growing, attractive, pink-flowered edging, hedging plant that was once used medicinally and is a favourite for edging knot gardens.

Its decorative qualities are really germander's main use today and germander edges to a path or border are neat and attractive, evergreen and compact.

Medicinally, it was once a major ingredient in a combination of herbs used for curing gout. Make a brew by steeping 125 ml (½ cup) leaves and flowers in 500 ml (2 cups) water for 10 minutes. Strain and drink daily until the condition is relieved. Taken as a tea it was believed to be a good brain stimulant and aided memory loss, but nowadays it seems to have been usurped by more favoured herbs such as sage and rosemary.

Germander can be grown from seed but the seed must be fresh and it needs the warmth of summer in order to germinate well. An easier way is to take cuttings or divide up clumps in spring. It does well where it is not crowded by other plants and, although it can stand partial shade, it does better in full sun. The only soil it does not thrive in is clay or black turf – it likes good drainage and the clay-type soils hold moisture longer than germander likes or needs. In fact it does not need much water which is something to be considered in areas prone to water shortages and drought.

Germander can be clipped and trimmed and trimmings are useful dried and added to pot-pourris as they act as an insect repellent. Because of its oils, germander usually remains ailment and insect free.

GINGER

PLATE 12

Family:	*Zingiberaceae*
Species:	*Zingiber officinale*
Plant:	perennial
Height:	up to 120 cm
Soil:	rich, well-drained
Exposure:	partial shade
Propagation:	rhizome, cuttings
Uses:	medicinal, condiment
Meaning:	excitement

Ginger is indigenous to China, South East Asia and West Africa and is cultivated all over the world. As well as being a popular condiment, it also has amazing medicinal properties and is easy to grow in the garden as a special interest plant. Its properties are stimulating, warming, digestive and aromatic. Even the flowers have a heady perfume that combines well with tuberoses and honeysuckle in an exotic pot-pourri.

Ginger is a wonderful general tonic and will also dispel worms, aid digestion and combat urinary infections and diarrhoea, while chewing a small piece of root will help in overcoming nausea and car-sickness. It is effective for regulating delayed or irregular menstruation and for relieving exhaustion during or following childbirth. In most of these cases a small piece of ginger the size of a marble may be chewed before meals.

A tea can be made using 1 ml (¼ tsp) powdered ginger to 500 ml (2 cups) boiling water, sweetened with honey and adding a slice of lemon. This is a wonderfully soothing drink at bedtime for colds and sore throats as well as menstrual problems. It is also beneficial for asthma and cramps in the feet.

Pieces of rhizome with an eye can be planted in rich, well-composted soil with good drainage. Space at least 45 cm apart and water until the new shoots push through. Every second spring divide the rhizomes if the clump becomes too straggly or overgrown and cut back flowering heads to encourage new flowers. Ginger does need frost protection in cold areas so cover well with grass and in spring cut off the stems that have died back. In warm areas, particularly coastal gardens, ginger is a lush perennial that gives much pleasure. It makes an interesting patio plant and can be planted in a tub where it will grow quite happily if it is watered well and the drainage is checked. Feed with compost every 4 months, and divide when the pot becomes too full, replacing with new soil.

GOLDEN ROD

PLATE 12

Family: *Compositae*
Species: *Solidago virgaurea*
Plant: perennial
Height: up to 1 metre
Soil: average, not too rich
Exposure: sun
Propagation: root division
Uses: medicinal
Meaning: precaution

Golden rod is another of the old-fashioned plants not often seen in modern gardens, but as it is so widely used in medicines and ointments perhaps we ought to find space for this plant with its eye-catching yellow spikes.

It is used in homoeopathic medicine for many ailments, including digestive problems, kidney and bladder infections, hayfever, respiratory infections and eye ailments. Golden rod is also famous for treating wounds, and the Saracens refused to go into battle without quantities of golden rod for dressings. The American Indians have used it as a tonic remedy for many decades, while even in the Middle Ages it was a famed herb for gangrene, and used then too for bladder and kidney infections.

It can be used just as effectively today: make a brew by pouring 500 ml (2 cups) boiling water over 2 handfuls of leaves and flowering tips and allow to stand. Strain and take 25 ml (2 tbls) of this mixture morning and night. This brew can be used to staunch bleeding and wash wounds and, taken at frequent intervals throughout the day, it will also bring down a fever. Golden rod tea is both pleasant tasting and a wonderful digestive tonic. It is made by using 25 ml (2 tbls) chopped leaves and flowers to 250 ml (1 cup) boiling water. Strain and sweeten with honey.

Propagate by division. Replant pieces of rooted stems into well-dug soil that has a very light dressing of compost – one spadeful to a square metre. Water until well established and thereafter water only once a week. Cut back faded flower-heads to ground level and divide clumps every second spring. The flowering heads last well in water but take care if you suffer from hayfever as the flowers are heavy with pollen.

GRANADILLA

PLATE 13

Family:	*Passifloraceae*
Species:	*Passiflora edulis* (passion fruit)
Plant:	perennial climber
Height:	up to 9 metres
Soil:	fairly rich, well-drained
Exposure:	sun, afternoon shade
Propagation:	seeds
Uses:	medicinal, culinary
Meaning:	religious superstition

The granadilla is a beautiful evergreen climber that clothes walls, pergolas and fences with rich green magic. It is one of the most prominent of the mystical flowers traditionally associated with the crucifixion and its symbolism is perhaps worth a small digression. The Spanish friars in America were the first to see in the granadilla flower the representation of the crucifixion. Then Monardes, a botanist and physician of the sixteenth century, put down in writing the first symbolic interpretation of the flower.

In the centre of the flower a pillar or column of the cross can be seen. The corona is the crown of thorns or halo which encircled the Lord's head. The ten surrounding white petals suggest ten of the twelve apostles, excluding Judas who betrayed Christ and Peter who denied Him. The five anthers are the hammers and the five wounds and the three stigmas are the three big nails that pierced His feet and hands.

The tendrils are the cords that bound Him or the whips that lashed him, while the small seed vessel is the sponge filled with vinegar which was thrust at Him to quench His thirst. The digitate leaves typify the hands of the persecutors.

When the flower is half open it resembles a star and represents the star in the East seen by the three wise men which heralded the birth of Christ. The leaves have three lobes, symbolising the Holy Trinity, the Father, the Son and the Holy Ghost. The purple colour in the flower suggests the purple robe that was placed on the Lord in mockery. The white colour in the flower symbolises the purity and light of the Saviour.

As the plant is a vine it signifies that the aspiring Christian needs to climb and the vine offers the support of the Lord's strength. The loneliness of Christ is typified by the single flowers which grow alone on the stems. The medicinal use of the granadilla, which is calming, quietening and soothing, symbolises the quietening and soothing of the heart when one has found the Lord.

The fruit of the granadilla is delicious and makes glorious puddings, drinks and cake flavourings. The juice is a digestive aid and is soothing for heartburn and dyspepsia. The leaves and flowers are used in homoeopathic medicine as a calming, soothing treatment for anxiety and nervous disorders.

Young seedlings are best started individually in small peat pots or small plastic bags and they should become well established before being planted in their permanent positions. Plant about 2 metres apart along an established fence or pergola. Once it is in position the granadilla does not like to be transplanted or have its roots disturbed by anything, such as poles being set into the soil beside it. It does need frost protection and a hessian tent over the vine during winter is advisable.

Apart from an occasional trimming or tying up of the long, trailing stems and a good weekly watering, the granadilla vine is undemanding and will give you many years of pleasure.

GRAPE

Family:	*Vitaceae*
Species:	*Vitis vinifera*
Plant:	perennial deciduous
Height:	up to 3,5 metres
Soil:	fairly rich, well-drained
Exposure:	sun
Propagation:	cuttings
Uses:	culinary, medicinal
Meaning:	life-blood or blood of life

The grapevine needs only the support of a fence, pole or trellis for it to be an attractive garden feature. The vine also has wonderful medicinal uses. The leaf can be used as a dressing for wounds and the juice of the leaf is an effective eye-wash diluted with water – 2 ml (½ tsp) juice to 20 ml (4 tsp) tepid water.

Fresh grape juice is used to treat rickets, anaemia and stomach and lymphatic ailments. It cleanses the blood, helps cure eczema, brings down fevers and helps to dissolve internal growths. A few tendrils chopped into a salad also makes a wonderful tonic. A general brew that can be used for all the above ailments is 2 large leaves and a few tendrils (3 or 4), chopped or crushed, to 250 ml (1 cup) boiling water. Steep and drink night and morning, sweetened with honey.

To make new vines from an established one cut lengths of about 30 cm from pruned-off stems in July and August. Fill a deep tub with sand and press the cuttings into it, covering 3 or 4 buds with the sand. Press down firmly and keep well watered until the new green buds show in spring. During these first few weeks do not allow the soil to dry out and keep fairly moist while the new vine establishes itself.

When the plant is strong, plant out into a deep hole which has had several spadefuls of compost mixed into it. Place the vine into the hole and stamp the soil down well around the roots. Make a large dam around it and give a good weekly watering. Tie up the long stems at intervals and train over a pergola or fence. In July start pruning back to neaten and cut out weak stems. The vine needs a hearty dressing of compost and old manure and a deep weekly watering throughout August and September – an extra bonus for the crop of grapes which will ripen in February and March.

HOLLYHOCK

PLATE 13

Family:	*Malvaceae*
Species:	*Althaea rosea*
Plant:	biennial
Height:	up to 2 metres
Soil:	fairly rich, friable
Exposure:	sun
Propagation:	seeds
Uses:	landscape, medicinal
Meaning:	ambition

The flowers and leaves of the hollyhock, a plant often cultivated for its considerable beauty, provide an extract that is used to soothe throat and mouth inflammations.

One of the oldest plants in cultivation, the hollyhock reached Europe from its native China in the sixteenth century, after which it was used as a medicinal and a pot herb.

There is a wide range of colours, varying from the original rose pink to a deeper crimson, cream and purple, and double and single flowers of variegated colours are now available in the hybridised forms. The double purple flowers, dried, may be used to colour wine and herb vinegars. Use several or just a couple of flowers per bottle, depending on your preference, and place in the sun for 3 days. Then strain and pour into clean bottles. A lavender vinegar can be coloured with only one or two flowers to give it an attractive mauve tinge.

Lightly boiled hollyhock leaves can be used as a worm remedy for children and leaves heated in wine can be taken to avert a miscarriage. Another brew made of the leaves soothes the digestive tract and aids certain female disorders, such as inflammation of the uterus and threatened miscarriage. Take a handful of leaves to 300 ml (½ pt) boiling water, add one to two buds and flowers, flavour with a pinch of cinnamon and ginger and steep until cool. Take 25 ml (2 tbls) four times daily.

Externally a lotion made from boiling two handfuls of leaves in 300 ml (½ pt) water for 10 minutes (keeping the pot covered) can be applied to wounds and inflamed areas. Alternatively, young leaves (not the rough undersides) warmed in hot water, directly applied to the painful area, are also effective.

Althaea rosea is easily raised from seed, sown where it is to grow. It tolerates most soils, needing only a little compost in its second spring and regular weekly watering.

In spring plant seeds 60 cm apart in well-dug soil. Add a light dressing of compost and water well. Cover the seeds lightly with a thin layer of sand and compost mixture and keep shaded with hessian stretched over the seed bed and supported on sticks so that it does not touch the bed. As the seedlings grow sturdier, remove the hessian and mulch around the plants with compost; this helps retain the moisture in the hot months of early summer. As hollyhock is a biennial, I plant such quick growing annuals among and around them as lemon-drop marigolds or forget-menots to give colour to the bed while the hollyhock matures.

In its second spring the hollyhock will send up a spike of beautiful flowers that will give pleasure all summer long. Once it has finished flowering the plant dies, so save the seed for next summer and throw the spent plant on the compost heap.

Hollyhock seeds itself readily and if the seedlings are transplanted early while they are still small they will do well. It has a long tap root, however, and does not like to be moved.

HONEYSUCKLE

PLATE 13

Family: *Caprifoliaceae*
Species: *Lonicera periclymenum*
Plant: perennial climber
Height: up to 3 metres
Soil: average
Exposure: sun, partial shade
Propagation: cuttings, rooted runners
Uses: medicinal, fragrance
Meaning: generous and devoted affection

This beautiful creeper is another of nature's apothecary shops all in one. The whole plant is medicinal and the fragrant flowers are glorious in pillow sachets and pot-pourris.

The flowers are an excellent treatment for asthma. Combine with equal parts of honey and molasses and take 1 tablespoon morning and night. A tea made from a handful of flowers in 250 ml (1 cup) boiling water and sipped early in the morning is excellent for soothing sore throats, and easing stiffness in the joints, rheumatism and arthritis.

Honeysuckle flowers can be preserved in honey for use in the winter. I pack a jar with flowers and pour just enough honey over them to cover them. The honey preserves the flowers and they can be taken out and used for teas to treat sore throats at any time of the year.

Crushed leaves, warmed in hot water, can be applied to wounds and sores and will aid in the healing process and a brew made from a handful of leaves to 1 litre (4 cups) boiling water clears skin rashes if used as a wash daily.

Honeysuckle covers banks, fences, arbours and shade houses and needs no attention other than the initial training up its support. It should be tied to the support and the unruly tendrils trimmed. Thereafter it will only give pleasure, covering the area with beautiful leaves and flowers.

Wherever a tendril touches the ground it will send down roots and these can be cut away and replanted. If kept moist for a few days until it is established, the runner will soon perk up and grow quickly.

Apart from an occasional watering, honeysuckle is undemanding and the heady fragrance of the flowers on a midsummer morning somehow sets the day right. A vase of honeysuckle will fill a room with its perfume. Save every flower for pot-pourris and scented sachets. Combined with roses and carnations, honeysuckle is a delightful ingredient in pot-pourris.

1 Garlic *p 57*
2 Geranium (scented) *p 119*
3 Wild pineapple (eucomis) *p 136*

1 Germander *p 58*
2 Ginger *p 59*
3 Golden rod *p 60*

1 Granadilla *p 61*
2 Hollyhock *p 64*
3 Honeysuckle *p 66*

1

2

1 Horehound *p 67*
2 Hydrangea *p 68*

HOREHOUND

PLATE 14

Family:	*Labiatae*
Species:	*Marrubium vulgare*
Plant:	perennial
Height:	30–60 cm
Soil:	poor, dry
Exposure:	sun
Propagation:	seeds, cuttings
Uses:	medicinal, culinary

The grey-green horehound is a perennial relative of mint and is an attractive plant if it is kept trimmed back and neatened.

It is an age-old medication for coughs and colds and the ancient Greeks used it as a poison antidote. Laid across doorways it was supposed to keep spiders and scorpions away. It is a wonderful insect repellent because of its bitterness.

I have never found horehound an invasive or aggressive grower but I have heard it said that it is vigorous and inclined to overrun its boundaries. In California it loves the climate so much that it has become a naturalised weed! It loves dry, sunny, rocky soil and needs to be planted 30 cm apart.

Horehound tea, a soothing drink for sore throats, is made by using 4 leaves to 250 ml (1 cup) boiling water. Drink half of it and gargle with the other half. A squeeze of lemon helps a little to relieve the bitterness.

Horehound candy was a very popular sore throat remedy. It is full of goodness, is pleasant to suck and is quite natural and harmless.

HOREHOUND CANDY

375 ml (1½ cups) fresh horehound leaves
500 ml (2 cups) boiling water
750 ml (3 cups) brown sugar
2 ml (½ tsp) cream of tartar
12,5 ml (1 tbls) lemon juice
lemon rind, grated

Make a strong infusion with horehound leaves and boiling water. Strain after 10 minutes into a large pot. Add sugar and cream of tartar. Boil to the hard crack stage of 300°F on a sweet-making thermometer. At this stage add the lemon juice and grated lemon rind. Pour into a buttered pan or ovenproof dish. Mark off into squares as it begins to harden. When it shrinks enough to turn out of the pan, sprinkle with a little powdered sugar (I use white sugar rolled with a rolling pin). Place in a strong plastic bag and break it up by gently tapping with the handle of a knife. Keep the candy in the bag so as not to let it absorb moisture and package into a plastic bag. Shake out the extra sugar and seal well. Do not attempt this on a rainy day!

HYDRANGEA

PLATE 14

Family:	*Hydrangeaceae*
Species:	*Hydrangea macrophylla* (Christmas rose) *H. arborescens*
Plant:	perennial
Height:	up to 2 metres
Soil:	fairly rich, moist
Exposure:	shade (does well on south-facing walls), can take sun
Propagation:	cuttings
Uses:	landscape, medicinal
Meaning:	heartlessness

This shade-loving plant needs a good deal of water for its full beauty to emerge. At Christmas time in the South African summer heat, bowls of blue, mauve and pink hydrangeas give a feeling of soothing coolness to a room and draw the eye.

The hydrangea was once a favourite herb of the Cherokee Indians for its soothing properties and it is indeed effective for urinary troubles and rheumatic and glandular disorders, as well as in the treatment of malaria.

The standard brew is 2 handfuls of young leaves in 300 ml (½ pt) boiling water; stand, then pour off and drink 2 dessertspoonfuls morning and night. This dose is helpful for easing all forms of rheumatism, including its chronic forms, and stiffness of the joints. Taken at the first sign of kidney and bladder infections, including kidney stones and backache from kidney troubles, this brew will soothe and heal. The same brew is of benefit for lymphatic swellings and glandular fever and in the old days was used in the treatment of dropsy.

Cuttings can be taken at any time of the year from old flowering stems. Cut off the flower and cut pieces about 15 cm long with several segments in the length. Press these into wet sand and keep moist until the new leaves appear. Plant out when well established, 1 metre apart. I usually put two or three cuttings a few centimetres apart in a group so that should one die I still have a sturdy one left, and they will be part of the same bush eventually. Water well and cut back the spent flowers in autumn. These can be dried effectively and mature flowers can be treated with glycerine and water (one third to two thirds) to which a little Prussian blue has been added for winter decorations.

If you bury a few used torch batteries near the roots this is said to bring out the beautiful blue colour we so often seek. Crush the battery a little with a spade. If the soil is acid the flowers will be blue, pink if the soil is alkaline.

HYSSOP

PLATE 15

Family:	*Labiatae*
Species:	*Hyssopus officinalis*
Plant:	perennial
Height:	30–60 cm
Soil:	well-drained, alkaline
Exposure:	sun, can take partial shade
Propagation:	cuttings, division
Uses:	medicinal
Meaning:	cleanliness

Hyssop is a shrubby, compact perennial which is an asset in any garden. It is known as a purification herb and there are a number of references to hyssop in the Bible, although there is some doubt as to whether the hyssop we know today is in fact the one referred to. David prayed he would be purged and cleansed by hyssop and it was given to lepers to purify them. Jesus was given a sponge dipped in vinegar and hyssop to quench His thirst during His crucifixion.

Hyssop leaves sprinkled over fatty fish during baking or grilling makes an interesting flavouring and absorbs some of the fattiness.

The oil from hyssop is used in perfumery and is an ingredient in eau-de-Cologne. This same oil has wonderful healing properties and is useful in the treatment of catarrh, coughs and colds and asthma. It will also strengthen a weak stomach and soothe and aid digestion.

As the oil is virtually unobtainable, the easiest way to use hyssop is to make a tea by steeping one flowering sprig the length of your thumb (or two thumb-length non-flowering twigs) in 250 ml (1 cup) boiling water. Stand for 2 or 3 minutes and then drink at least 250 ml (1 cup) daily. You can use it as a gargle too. A bunch of hyssop of about 10 sprigs (flowers included) added to a hot bath will soothe rheumatism. Bruised leaves make a soothing poultice for a cut or wound. Place the leaves on a square of gauze and bind it in place with a crêpe bandage. Change the dressing every few hours and replace the old leaves with new ones.

The hyssop tea is another wonderful treatment for rheumatism – 500 ml (2 cups) taken daily will bring relief; sweeten with honey if desired. Hyssop also dries well and can be used for teas during the winter, 5–10 ml (1–2 tsp) per cup.

Hyssop also reduces perspiration if taken as a tea regularly and it is a wonderful herb for treating a black eye! Warm a handful of leaves and flowers by pouring hot water over them. As hot as is bearable gently place over the black eye. Hold in place with a warm towel for a few minutes, then repeat 2 or 3 times.

Hyssop is best propagated by cuttings rooted in sand. It makes an attractive border around a vegetable garden or in a knot garden. It will bloom one year after planting and the flowers will be pink, mauve, purple or white. As a cut flower it lasts well in the vase and dried leaves and flowers act as a fixative in pot-pourris. Its strong, not unpleasant aroma makes it valuable in the vegetable garden where it

69

will protect cabbages against the cabbage butterfly. It can take partial shade and is economical to grow as a long-lasting perennial.

As the plant responds well to pruning it can be trimmed twice during the summer and will make a sturdy and attractive low hedge. Each piece that is trimmed off can be dried and used in cooking to add a deliciously different flavour. Tie up bunches of trimmings in muslin bags and use in the bath.

Hyssop is one of the butterfly herbs and bees love it too. The mauve flowered variety, which is the true hyssop, seems to attract them the most.

In each August the established plants can be dug up and divided. Plant 60 cm apart in soil into which a rich dressing of compost has been dug – about 3 spadefuls to one square metre. Water well twice a week to establish the new plants.

70

IRIS

PLATE 15

Family:	*Iridaceae*
Species:	*Iris versicolor*, *I. germanica* (blue flag), *I. germanica* var *florentina* (orris root)
Plant:	perennial
Height:	up to 75 cm
Soil:	average, fairly moist
Exposure:	sun, partial shade
Propagation:	rhizomes
Uses:	medicinal, fixative
Meaning:	message

Formerly the iris was much cultivated in herb gardens for its medicinal properties and for its dried, pounded root which was used as a fixative in pot-pourris. The *Iris germanica* var *florentina* is the treasured orris root of herbalists and perfumers; the sweet-scented powder is a fixative and its violet fragrance blends beautifully with other flower fragrances or essences.

Iris means 'rainbow' in Greek, and the flower is so named for its varying hues. The old-fashioned deep purple and white irises are the ones most often used medicinally.

The plant is a mild general tonic for the whole body but its biggest benefit is to the liver. The rhizome, which is the medicinal part, should be cut up into thin cross pieces (choose one about 15 cm in length). Steep these in a bottle of red wine for 24 hours. The dose is one table-spoon three times a day before meals. This tonic is beneficial for jaundice and all liver ailments, it builds and purifies the blood, helps get rid of skin blemishes caused by a sluggish liver and gastro-intestinal system and is effective in relieving constipation. The brew is mildly laxative and it stimulates the flow of saliva, bile and gastric secretions. *Large doses cause nausea so treat with care*.

Leaves warmed in hot water, and held in place with a warm towel, can be applied externally to bruises.

The iris does well in partial shade and it does like a lot of water. In fact many species are actually bog plants, growing lushly in damp places.

Propagation is by rhizomes. Prepare a bed by digging a lavish amount of compost and old, well-rotted manure deep into the soil. Space rhizomes 30 cm apart and place in the soil (not too deep), pressing down well. A deep watering twice a week should be sufficient for their needs. Divide the clumps every two years; any extra rhizomes can be ground up fresh and then dried and used as a fixative in pot-pourris.

IVY

PLATE 16

Family:	*Araliaceae*
Species:	*Hedera helix*
Plant:	perennial climber
Height:	climbs up to 6 metres, spreads up to 6 metres
Soil:	any
Exposure:	prefers shade, can take sun
Propagation:	rooted cuttings, cuttings
Uses:	landscape, medicinal
Meaning:	fidelity

Ivy is a valuable asset in any herb garden. It is always attractive, growing in shady corners or under shrubs.

Its medicinal uses are many and varied. It is used in the treatment of headaches, ear and eye infections, mumps, glandular fever, swollen joints and jaundice. However, it is a potent herb so care should be taken in using it. Ten leaves to 1 litre (4 cups) boiling water is the recommended dosage; this can also be used as an eye-wash.

Crushed leaves that have been soaked in salt and vinegar overnight make a good dressing for corns as they soften the corn so that it can be removed easily. Chopped leaves in hot water make a soothing poultice for sciatica.

Be sure that you choose the correct hedera variety. Ivy comes in many shapes and sizes and it is only the old-fashioned evergreen *Hedera helix* that is the medicinal one. The variegated and large-leafed varieties and the miniatures are actually poisonous if used medicinally so *extreme care must be taken before using ivy as a medicine*.

A few sprays of ivy root themselves so easily in a glass jar that you will have no trouble propagating. A long trailing stem can be pinned into the ground by a stone and a handful of earth and it will soon take root. The spray can then be clipped off and left to establish itself; later it can be dug out and replanted elsewhere.

Ivy makes a good pot-plant too and is beautiful in a hanging basket. Cuttings root easily at any time of the year and, apart from needing trimming from time to time, ivy is undemanding and always rewarding.

JOB'S TEARS

PLATE 16

Family:	*Gramineae*
Species:	*Coix lacryma-jobi*
Plant:	perennial
Height:	30–60 cm
Soil:	average or poor, well-drained
Exposure:	full sun
Propagation:	seeds
Uses:	decorative, medicinal

Job's tear grass is such an interesting plant to have in the garden that we should make more use of it. It grows with ease and abundance along the Natal coast and the Zulus make necklaces from the seeds for the tourist market. It is believed that the wearer of a Job's tear will be protected.

A fermented drink, used with effectiveness for bronchitis and catarrhal infections, can be made from the half-ripened seeds of Job's tears. The seeds are also used for treating kidney and bladder infections and for dysentery. The dosage is 6 half-ripened seeds, crushed and pounded, to 250 ml (1 cup) boiling water; a wineglassful should be taken three times a day.

To get a head start with Job's tears plant one or two seeds in a pellet pot and keep moist and warm during July and August. Then plant out in the garden, about 60 cm apart, when all danger of frost is past. If the seed is soaked in warm water overnight (I fill a thermos with warm (not hot) water and keep it closed to maintain the warmth) the seed will sprout in about 3 weeks.

Gather the seed-heads as they ripen and thread them on nylon fishing line to make rosaries, necklaces and teething bracelets for babies.

Winter frosts will dry the plant off but, like grass, it rejuvenates itself in spring. I always make sure to keep a few seeds to safeguard against a particularly bitter winter where the plant might be lost.

LAVENDER

PLATE 16

Family:	*Labiatae*
Species:	*Lavandula spica* (English lavender), *L. spica* 'Munstead', *L. vera* (Dutch lavender), *L. dentata* (French lavender), *L. latifolia*
Plant:	perennial
Height:	30–120 cm
Soil:	dry, well-drained
Exposure:	sun
Propagation:	seeds, cuttings
Uses:	fragrance, medicinal
Meaning:	distrust

Lavender is surely the most traditional herb garden plant and no herb garden is complete without a lavender bush or two. The most widely used variety is the English lavender, *Lavandula spica*. This grows woody and tall and can be clipped into a neat shape at the end of the summer. Frost can affect the lavender bush and I cover mine with grass in winter. In spring any tips that the frost has caught can be cut away and the new growth is quick and vigorous. Cuttings can be pulled from the stems at any time of the year except during the coldest months. Be sure that a heel is torn off with the cutting and press securely into wet sand. In April and May make a polythene tent to put over the cutting tray to keep it protected and moist. In June, July and August all cuttings benefit from a plastic tent as it acts as a miniature hothouse; the newly rooted plants stand a better chance of developing if they are well protected against cold winds and chilly nights.

Two dwarf varieties are available in South Africa, *L. vera* (Dutch lavender) and *L. spica* 'Munstead'. These grow to 30 cm in height, less in width, and they both make good edging plants in an aromatic section of the herb garden. Their flowering spikes are particularly beautiful and butterflies love them. Pick them for the vase and allow them to dry, then use them in sachets and pot-pourris.

Like sage, lavender has the habit of suddenly dying off from no obvious cause; sometimes just a portion of the bush will die back and this can be cut away and will soon be replaced by new growth. When the whole bush dies, however, it is best to dig it up. Remove the soil around the root area, replacing it with fresh soil, sandy and light, dig in a little compost and then plant a new bush in its place. Because of this problem of unexpected dying off I always try to have a few cuttings or seedlings growing strongly as a standby.

Lavandula dentata is the French lavender. It is a showy plant and reaches about 90 cm in height. It has bright green serrated leaves and the flowers grow in blunt clusters, each topped with a tuft of petal-like bracts. It seems to grow easily and flowers continuously in most gardens. It does need to be cut back after the midsummer flowers for new growth to take place before the cold months. Use the flowers in pot-pourris but this variety has no medicinal use so grow it only for its beauty and fragrance.

Spike lavender or *Lavandula latifolia* is beautifully fragrant and puts out long flowering stems in midsummer that are often branched. Let the flowers mature before picking them. They can then be bound with raffia and hung in bunches in a cool shed until dry. Once the flowers have been removed save the stalks for burning on winter fires and their scent will fill the whole house.

Lavender tea is made by pouring 250 ml (1 cup) boiling water over a thumb-length sprig of leaves and sweetening with honey. It can be taken to relieve a headache, soothe over-exhaustion and excitement, promote sleep and quieten nervousness and anxiety.

A lavender-stuffed pillow also aids sleep and will soothe and calm a restless child. Old-fashioned lavender water, which was used to revive fainting ladies, is also a refreshing mouth-wash. Even a few drops on a handkerchief held over the brow will do much to relieve a headache.

Lavender sachets hung in a linen cupboard will keep your linen smelling fresh and they are easily made:

10 parts lavender leaves and flowers
2 parts powdered lemon peel
1 part powdered orris root
1 part powdered cinnamon
1 part powdered cloves

Mix well and seal in a crock or jar. Shake daily for 2 weeks, then fill your sachets or pillows.

Seed germinates easily if sown in river sand and kept damp. Plant out 90 cm apart (45 cm apart for *L. vera* and *L. spica* 'Munstead').

75

LEMON BALM (MELISSA)

PLATE 4

Family:	*Labiatae*
Species:	*Melissa officinalis*
Plant:	hardy perennial
Height:	30–60 cm
Soil:	moist, rich
Exposure:	filtered shade
Propagation:	cuttings, division
Uses:	culinary, fragrance, medicinal
Meaning:	sympathy

This is a most rewarding mint to grow as it is a pretty garden plant and has many health-giving and culinary uses. Hot melissa tea will lift the spirits and calm and settle nervous disorders; it is also beneficial for coughs and colds. Use one or two thumb-length sprigs to 250 ml (1 cup) boiling water, sweeten with honey and sip at bed-time; it also helps cure insomnia.

Melissa leaves are also an ingredient in pot-pourris and they produce a fragrant oil which is used in the perfume industry. Bunches of leaves hung in cupboards will deter moths.

To help cows regain their strength after calving, give them a mixture of melissa and marjoram (a handful of each boiled in 2 litres (8 cups) water).

The leaves can also be used in fruit salads and in making a delicious, cooling summer drink. Pour a litre (4 cups) of boiling water over a handful of leaves, cool, and add the juice of 2 lemons and 1 litre (4 cups) of clear apple juice. Add a little honey to sweeten if necessary and serve chilled with a few fresh leaves and slices of lemon.

Melissa is an easy plant to grow, needing little attention. It is in fact one of my favourites, for it gives so much in return for so little care. At the end of summer the straggly growth should be cut away and encroaching plants lifted and separated out into new areas. It is not a prolific spreader. The tender leaves need shade (you will find full sun burns them) and, but for an occasional spadeful of compost and a good watering, melissa will thrive beautifully.

New plants can be made by taking cuttings of new growth in midsummer and pressing into sand. By keeping a uniform moisture for a week or two these will root in no time. Plant out 30 cm apart and keep damp for the first two or three weeks. Thereafter water twice a week.

LEMON VERBENA

PLATE 16

Family: *Verbenaceae*
Species: *Aloysia triphylla* (syn *Lippia citriodora*)
Plant: perennial
Height: 1,8 metres
Soil: average, well-drained
Exposure: full sun
Propagation: cuttings
Uses: fragrance, medicinal
Meaning: kindness

Surely no other shrub has the intense fragrance of the lemon verbena. Used in pot-pourris and pillows, it remains fragrant for many years. Medicinally it is an anti-spasmodic drink: make a tea with 4 leaves to 250 ml (1 cup) boiling water, and drink after a meal. It is also good for flatulence and easing indigestion and makes a delicious cooling summer drink with lemon juice. Simply add a squeeze of lemon juice (about 60 ml or 4 tbls) to a brew made from 4 lemon verbena leaves to 250 ml (1 cup) boiling water. Sweeten with honey, cool and serve with a cube of ice.

Lemon verbena needs adequate protection in frost areas where it will also lose its leaves in winter; in sub-tropical zones, however, it can be treated as an evergreen.

The bush may become straggly with age and benefits from a good trim or cut back. Save every twig for sachets and pot-pourris or for placing in the linen cupboard just as it is, fresh and green. As it dries it will scent the linen with its lemon freshness and it is the only herb which will prevent the formation of mildew.

Cuttings can be taken in spring and throughout summer. Choose woody pieces with a small heel, trim off excess leaves and press into wet sand. Keep cool, shaded, moist and protected and plant into bags when rooted to establish a sturdy plant. It grows as wide as it is tall so allow plenty of space between the bushes.

This pretty shrub also benefits from a good spray of water every now and then. Cut off flowering tips if you want it to become thick and bushy and trim it regularly. Strong winds can break the branches so stake them if they seem too heavy or long.

LOVAGE

Family: *Umbelliferae*
Species: *Levisticum officinale*
Plant: hardy perennial
Height: 1–1,2 metres
Soil: moist, cool
Exposure: semi-shade
Propagation: seeds, root stock
Uses: culinary, medicinal
Meaning: interest

Lovage is a close relative of celery, but it is four times its size. The whole plant is used for flavouring savoury dishes and it can be dried and used in mixed herb sachets or in bouquet garni bags. Fresh or dried, it always imparts a delicious flavour, but it is strong so use it sparingly.

Its medicinal value lies in soothing coughs and treating stomach disorders. In Roman times the seeds and leaves were chopped into salads to help over-burdened stomachs on feast days! The stems can be cooked on their own as a vegetable or, added to a pot of new peas, they make a mouth-watering dish served with a dab of butter and a squeeze of lemon juice.

Lovage is grown easily from seed, sown in trays in March for planting out in September. The plants do not seem to mind being moved and I have several times moved them to various positions; providing you take a big spadeful of soil from around the root, the plant does not even wilt. Lovage does prefer a shady position and well-composted soil that retains moisture. Dig in a little compost each season to stimulate new growth. As it dies down in winter, pick and dry several bunches to use for soups and stews in winter. Dry on newspaper in the shade, then store in well-stoppered glass bottles in a dark cupboard.

Watch out for lovage plants in local nurseries. They really are worth buying for seed in South Africa is not yet readily available.

LUCERNE (ALFALFA)

PLATE 17

Family: *Leguminosae*
Species: *Medicago sativa*
Plant: perennial
Height: 30–60 cm
Soil: rich, loamy
Exposure: sun
Propagation: seeds
Uses: medicinal, nutritious
Meaning: life

Lucerne or alfalfa is such a useful, nutritious plant that it is worth including in our gardens. It is so trouble free, undemanding and attractive that I can't imagine why it is not used far more extensively.

Fresh leaves can be used in salads and can also be used with lemon juice to make a refreshing summer drink.

LUCERNE SUMMER DRINK

6–8 thumb-length tops
1 litre (4 cups) boiling water
juice of 3 lemons
37,5 ml (1 dessertsp) honey

Pour the boiling water over the lucerne. Allow to steep and cool. Blend in lemon juice and honey. Serve with ice.

Lucerne is an excellent tonic, alkalizing the system and cleansing the kidneys. A tea can be made by steeping 3 thumb-length sprigs of lucerne in 250 ml (1 cup) boiling water. Drink a wineglassful three times a day.

I have recently been told of an effective cold remedy using one handful of lucerne leaves and twigs and 900 ml (4½ cups) boiling water. Pour the water over the lucerne, let it stand for 30 minutes, then strain off one cupful and drink it hot. Do this 3 or 4 times during the day and the next day the cold will be gone. Repeat the procedure for 3 days, however, or the cold is liable to return.

As it has a deep root system lucerne does not like to be transplanted and it really is best to sow a few seeds in ready prepared soil that has been well watered. Mulch with leaves and grass and peg a plastic tent around it to keep it from drying out. Within 3 or 4 days it will sprout but be sure not to let it dry out as it needs constant moisture in these first weeks. Keep mulched and remove the protective tent once the plant is a few centimetres high.

I cut back old flowering stalks to encourage new growth. If you love butterflies a lucerne bush will attract them to your garden. In the rainy season lucerne plants seed themselves. Transplant the new seedlings when just big enough to handle (the smaller the better as they do not transplant well).

MAIDENHAIR FERN

PLATE 17

Family: *Adiantaceae*
Species: *Adiantum capillus-veneris*
Plant: perennial
Height: up to 60 cm
Soil: moist, rich, prefers being in a pot
Exposure: shade
Propagation: division, spores
Uses: decorative, medicinal
Meaning: fragile beauty

We are all familiar with the exquisitely delicate beauty of the maidenhair fern, a beloved indoor pot-plant. It seems to like its roots pot-bound and undisturbed. Often it almost looks too large for its pot but that is usually when it is happiest. It does not like being in draughts and it cannot tolerate sun for any length of time. Apart from an occasional feeding of a little compost and a good watering, maidenhair is undemanding.

Medicinally it is used for chest colds, coughs and pleurisy. Boil up 4 medium-sized leaves in 500 ml (2 cups) water and drink 2 dessert-spoons 3 times a day.

To aid hair loss, scalp infections and brittle and scanty hair, the same brew can be rubbed into the hair and scalp each night. Add a few drops of oil of lavender to the lotion. Two dessert-spoons taken morning and evening will also aid hair growth.

Maidenhair can be made into a drink, with sugar and water, called capillaire, once enjoyed by young ladies of the court.

Spores sometimes seed themselves in moist places in a greenhouse and, provided the tiny ferns are planted then, they will probably adapt to their new abode quite successfully. It really is very difficult to transplant a fully mature plant, though, as they do not like to be disturbed. With care a mature plant can be divided and planted immediately into fresh pots, hanging baskets or into shady corners in the herb garden. If kept watered and protected from draughts a measure of success is possible.

I keep pots of maidenhair fern in my herb garden in the shade areas rather than planted out into the ground as they seem to do better that way.

MARIGOLD

PLATE 18

Family:	*Compositae*
Species:	*Tagetes erecta* (African marigold)
Plant:	annual
Height:	15–90 cm
Soil:	average, well-drained
Exposure:	sun
Propagation:	seeds
Uses:	insecticide, landscape
Meaning:	vulgarity

In South Africa so many different marigold varieties can be seen sparkling in summer gardens. Edging a vegetable garden, they are a wonderful insect deterrent and a companion plant to many vegetables. If dug into the soil before planting potatoes, they rid the soil of nematodes and in fact experiments are currently being conducted on marigolds with regard to nematode infestation in the soil.

Marigold's native country is Mexico where it is known as the 'cloud plant' and the use of the foliage and flowers in teas and flavourings is as old as the Aztec culture itself. Leaves and flowers can be fed to chickens to give colour to their flesh and egg yolk, but be careful not to overfeed as you will upset their digestion!

Dried flowers and leaves can be added to insect repellent sachets and pot-pourris. A close relative of the marigold, khakibos, is invaluable as an insect repellent and its rather pungent scent becomes surprisingly pleasant when dried. Save each plant for the compost heap to rid it of unwanted egg-laying insects.

As a border plant the smaller varieties are easy to grow, uniform and attractive. They need a compost-rich soil to establish a lush early growth. Sow the seeds in trays or seed beds in August and keep well watered. Prepare a bed that is dug deeply and well composted – 3–4 spadefuls to 1 square metre. Water well and plant out the seedlings when big enough to handle. Shade them with a few leafy twigs pressed into the ground around the little plants for a few days. Keep moist until they become sturdy, then water well once a week or more frequently if they show signs of wilting in the summer heat. Plant 20–30 cm apart if they are the small variety and 60 cm apart if they are the tall, flowering variety.

MARJORAM

PLATE 18

Family:	*Labiatae*
Species:	*Origanum vulgare*
Plant:	perennial
Height:	30–60 cm
Soil:	not fussy, prefers sandier soil types
Exposure:	full sun
Propagation:	cuttings
Uses:	medicinal, culinary
Meaning:	blushes

Marjoram is a Mediterranean herb meaning 'joy of the mountain' and all over the world it is highly prized for its flavour-filled leaves and aroma. It has medicinal uses which add to its value, some of which include the treating of sore throats and colds, digestive problems and bed-wetting. Marjoram tea is a wonderful anti-depressant. Take a thumb-length twig and pour 250 ml (1 cup) boiling water over it. Steep, sweeten with honey and drink.

Marjoram prefers full sun but happily takes a bit of shade in the afternoons and it really does not mind what sort of soil it grows in except the heavier clay type.

It is easily grown from cuttings. Where branches touch the ground they will often send out rootlets and when these small branches are cut away and planted they usually take very easily. Cuttings from the previous year's growth can be taken in mid-summer or in spring, and kept in moist sand until rooted. They can then be planted out in the place where they are to remain but should be kept shaded for a few days.

Marjoram grows to a good sized bush, as broad as it is tall. The secret of keeping it looking good is to clip off the flowering stems as soon as they begin to look straggly. Clipped well back, in no time new growth will again round out the bush.

The dried seed-heads can be used as effectively as the leaves, but only in savoury herb mixes and bouquet garnis. Pick and dry on newspaper in the shade and in two or three days the leaves are usually dry enough to be rubbed off the stems and stored in crocks or bottles. Keep closed to ensure that they are dust free and use in meat, chicken, cheese and egg dishes. (Use approximately 5 ml (1 tsp) for a dish to serve 6 people.)

Marjoram also makes a beautiful container plant if planted in a large deep pot with good drainage.

1 Hyssop *p 69*
2 Iris *p 71*
3 St John's wort (hypericum) *p 125*

1 Ivy *p 72*
2 Job's tears *p 73*
3 Lavender *p 74*
4 Lemon verbena *p 77*

1 Lovage *p 78*
2 Lucerne (alfalfa) *p 79*
3 Maidenhair fern *p 80*

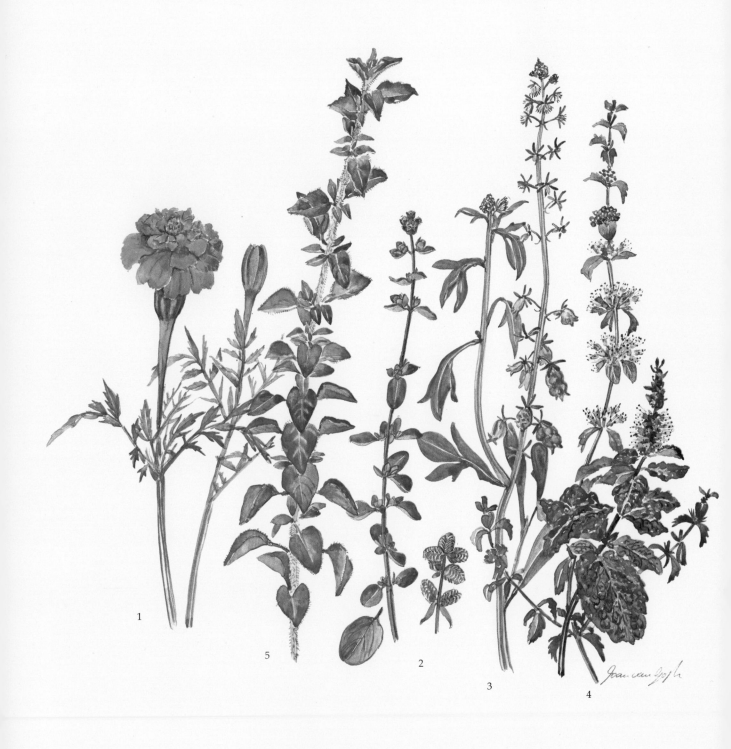

1
5
2
3
4

1 Marigold *p 81*
2 Marjoram *p 82*
3 Mignonette *p 83*
4 Mint *p 84*
5 Oreganum *p 96*

MIGNONETTE

PLATE 18

Family: *Resedaceae*
Species: *Reseda odorata*
Plant: annual, sometimes biennial
Height: up to 25 cm
Soil: any
Exposure: sun, likes afternoon shade
Propagation: seeds
Uses: fragrance, medicinal
Meaning: your qualities surpass your charms

This is another old-fashioned plant that is so beautifully fragrant it ought to have a place in the aromatic section of the garden. The word 'reseda' means 'to calm' and indicates the narcotic properties of the plant. Pillows stuffed with dried mignonette flowers are wonderfully sleep-invoking and a little lemon verbena and lavender added to them will give you a beautifully scented bedroom as well.

Tea made from mignonette soothes irritated nerves. Make a brew of 25 ml (2 tbls) flowers to 250 ml (1 cup) boiling water, steep, strain, sweeten with honey and drink just before going to sleep.

Flowers and leaves added to other wound-healing herbs such as yarrow enhance their pain-relieving properties and can also be used to wash out the wound. Mignonette is also an aid to asthma and hayfever, using 2 handfuls of flowers and leaves with 300 ml (½ pt) boiling water to make a brew. Allow to steep and drink 25 ml (2 tbls) three times a day. The same brew can also be used to wash out sore, red eyes.

As mignonette is low growing it makes a beautiful edging to a path and it is a wonderful plant for attracting bees. It germinates well from seed sown in August and it can be planted out in the garden in mid September. Sow seed in sand-filled trays, spacing them individually as far as possible, cover with fine compost and press well down. Keep moist and protected and harden off once the seedlings are nearing a handling size by allowing them sunlight for increasing periods each day. Plant out 20 cm apart in well-prepared soil that has had compost dug into it – 4 spadefuls to one square metre. Keep the seedlings shaded and well watered until they are established. Then water only once or twice a week, depending on the weather. On hot dry days they will benefit from a more frequent cool spray. If you cut off the faded flowering heads new heads will appear. Do this regularly and the plant will continue for a second season.

MINTS

Family:	*Labiatae*
Species:	*Mentha sauveolens variegata* (pineapple mint, golden apple mint), *M. sauveolens* (apple mint, Bowles mint), *M. citrata* (orange mint), *M. piperita* (peppermint), *M. requienii* (jewel mint, Corsican mint, peppermint lawn), *M. aquatica* (spearmint), *M. spicata* (common mint, garden mint)
Plant:	perennial
Height:	15–36 cm
Soil:	moist, rich
Exposure:	shade, can take sun
Propagation:	cuttings, division
Uses:	culinary, medicinal, fragrance
Meaning:	virtue

There is a wide assortment of mints which are so easily grown that I set aside a large section of the herb garden for my collection. In ancient Greek mythology when Pluto, god of the underworld, became enraptured with Menthe, a beautiful young nymph, his wife Proserpine, in a jealous rage, cursed Menthe and turned her into a herb, leaving her forever to grow in moist and shady places. But Menthe was much loved and the Greeks picked and used her fragrant leaves from that day to this, introducing her far and wide throughout the world.

In Biblical times the Pharisees paid taxes with mint leaves and ancient medicines recommended using mints for all sorts of conditions, including the bites of mad dogs and vipers, insect stings, mouth and gum infections and digestive problems!

Mint was also used to help skin diseases and to stimulate a failing appetite. As all the mint species share the special aroma and flavour it seems not to matter which variety is used as they are all effective.

Bunches of mint hung in the kitchen will keep flies out and peppermint rubbed onto the skin will keep mosquitoes away. Bruise the bunches from time to time, and replace them when they dry out.

Mints are extremely invasive and need to be contained. I use strips of thick black plastic, a method which has proved to be very effective. Strips about a third of a metre wide, dug vertically into a furrow, will prevent root invasion into neighbouring beds. Only a small piece need protrude and the lush growth of the mint soon camouflages it. If you do not separate the varieties, they will grow into one another and the not so vigorous mints, like black peppermint or eau de Cologne mint, will be swamped by the more vigorous growing apple mints and spearmints.

All mints need to be lifted and replanted in newly composted soil after three years. They send out runners, constantly looking for new soil, and old roots should be discarded and the new runners reset into the fresh soil. Cuttings can be taken from the new runners and, with just a little care, will make strong new plants in a short time. Mints do not like manure so prepare beds for mint only with compost and leaf mould. Mint in containers needs to be repotted each year, preferably in early spring, and container mint needs water daily for lush growth, as well as an occasional dressing of an organic plant food like marinure.

Mints cross pollinate quickly so if you want to keep the varieties separate be sure to keep the flowering heads cut so that the bees cannot easily go from one to the next.

All the mints are worth growing. There is much confusion and argument over names and there are varieties within varieties. I have chosen a few of the better known ones to discuss here, however, and I give only a general, common description.

Pineapple Mint

This is a particularly easy grower and when grown in the sun has more creamy yellow on the leaves than when the plant is grown in the shade. It is also known as golden apple mint and is a useful addition to pot-pourris. It reaches a height of about 60 cm and forms a rather attractive bushy growth if kept clipped back and trimmed. It is often used as a ground cover as it does not need much water.

A delicious dessert can be made using sprigs of pineapple mint:

PINEAPPLE MINT CREME

250 ml (1 cup) heavy cream
160 ml (2/3 cup) sugar
1 large tin crushed pineapple or pineapple chunks
25 ml ((2 tbls) gelatine
80 ml (1/3 cup) warm water
4 thumb-length sprigs pineapple mint

Strip the leaves from the stems of the pineapple mint and place with pineapple and sugar into a blender. Add the gelatine, which has been softened in the warm water, and whirl until well blended. Whisk cream in a large bowl until thick. Fold in the pureed pineapple blend, and pour into a glass bowl that has been rinsed in cold water. Top with candied mint leaves or garnish with fresh young mint leaves. Chill and serve.

Apple Mint, Bowles Mint

This mint is sometimes called dryland mint as it withstands drought and full sun well. It can grow up to 60 or 90 cm in height and has a furry, greyish-green leaf. It is used in sauces and for salad dressings and also makes a delicious tea.

Mint leaf candy is a tasy treat which is easy to make. The downy leaves take up the sugar and white of egg better than smooth-leaved varieties and they make a lovely decoration for cakes and puddings. Pineapple mint can also be used for mint candies.

MINT LEAF CANDY

1 egg, white only
water
castor sugar
apple mint leaves

Take whole mint leaves and brush well with the white of an egg which has been lightly beaten with a teaspoon of water. Dust with castor sugar and lay on wax paper. Leave to dry in a warm place.

Orange Mint

Orange mint prefers shade and a moist soil but I have grown it in the sun and, although not as prolific, it does do well. It reaches about 30 cm in height and is a vigorous grower.

The most useful of all the mints in pot-pourris and in sachets, it has an appealing orange-like fragrance.

It is delicious in fruit drinks and a few leaves chewed after meals also aids indigestion.

Peppermint

A familiar flavour, peppermint makes the best after-dinner drink, using one sprig to a pot of tea with a sachet of rooibos. Sweeten with honey. (Never use milk in herb teas.) Use peppermint in icecream, fruit drinks and as a decoration in fruit salads and desserts.

Jewel Mint, Corsican Mint, Peppermint Lawn

This precious, brilliant green creeping mint rarely grows over 2–3 cm high and forms a moss-like, incredibly fragrant mat.

A fresh handful of this mint tied in muslin and soaked in the bath will do much to ease fatigue and body aches and pains. I rub the small bundle all over my body and emerge from the bath feeling wonderfully fresh.

It is useful in pot-pourris but should not be used as a tea as it is too strong and bitter tasting.

Mentha requinii needs shade and moisture and can be kept going through winter in summer rainfall areas if it is watered every three days. A thin sprinkling of dried leaves spread over it (not so much as to smother it but enough to protect it from frost) will ensure a lush spring growth; never let it dry out or it will die.

Garden Mint, Common Mint

Mentha spicata is the common or garden mint used for mint sauce. It grows beautifully under a dripping tap and reaches a height of 30–60 cm.

The leaves can be dried for winter use as the mints die down in winter. Cut sprigs and dry in the shade on racks. Crumble off the stems when dry and discard; store the leaves in glass bottles. Use in sauces and jellies by soaking the leaves in a little warm water.

MINT JELLY

4 cups fresh mint leaves, well pressed down
1,5 litres (6 cups) boiling water
50 ml (2½ tbls) gelatine
250 ml (1 cup) sugar
250 ml (1 cup) lemon juice

Pour boiling water over mint. Allow to steep for 10 minutes. Strain. Dissolve gelatine in some of the warm liquid and add to the rest of the mint water. Dissolve sugar in the mixture, add lemon juice and stir well. Bottle in small screw-top jars and place in refrigerator to set. Then store in a cool cupboard and use as an accompaniment to roast mutton or pork dishes. (This jelly keeps for about 6 months.)

Spearmint

Mentha aquatica grows tall and robust, up to 90 cm, and has elongated leaves. It loves to have wet feet and seems to do well in full sun too. It sends out runners which transplant easily.

A delicious summer drink can be made from spearmint. Pour 2 litres (8 cups) boiling water over 4 handfuls of mint. Cool, strain and add 1 litre (4 cups) pure granadilla or pineapple juice. Add the pulp of 4 granadillas and half a chopped pineapple. Chill and serve with sprigs of fresh mint in a punch bowl. Add ice cubes at the last moment.

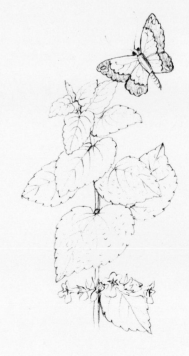

MULLEIN

PLATE 29

Family:	*Scrophulariaceae*
Species:	*Verbascum thapsus*
Plant:	biennial
Height:	up to 2 metres
Soil:	friable, fairly rich
Exposure:	sun
Propagation:	seeds
Uses:	medicinal, landscape

Mullein is an easy, undemanding plant to grow and if it is treated as a biennial it makes a beautiful yellow spire of flowers in the herb garden in its second year. If you want to keep it longer than that do not allow it to flower. It seems to seed itself with ease and once you have a mature plant that has ripening seeds you will never be without a few new plants in the garden the following season.

The flowering spike, which is known as 'Our Lady's taper', can be dipped when dry into melted fat and lit and it makes a novel garden light at a braai.

A brew made from the leaf and flower is a soothing remedy for chest ailments such as pneumonia and bronchitis, and a homoeopathic oil is made from mullein for treating earache. It is also a remedy for enuresus (bed-wetting), urinary infections and bowel complaints. The dosage is 250 ml (1 cup) chopped leaves and flowers to 500 ml (2 cups) boiling water. Steep for 10 minutes, strain and drink 1 wineglassful of this brew 3 or 4 times daily.

Mullein is an attractive old-fashioned plant and its grey rosette of leaves, furry and soft, wrapped around the feet in winter will keep them remarkably warm!

Sow seeds in individual peat pots or small bags in sandy soil and keep moist and protected. When the seedlings have 4–6 leaves they can be planted out in the garden. Harden off first by gradually giving them more sun each day until they are strong enough to plant in their position of full sun. Space the plants 60 cm apart and plant in deeply dug soil that has some old manure and compost added to it. Water well and thereafter water once weekly. They need no further attention.

MUSTARD

PLATE 19

Family:	*Cruciferae*
Species:	*Brassica nigra*
Plant:	annual
Height:	30–90 cm
Soil:	average
Exposure:	sun
Propagation:	seeds
Uses:	culinary, medicinal
Meaning:	indifference

Mustard is an important tonic and antiseptic herb and its medicinal uses have been practised and praised for many years. A few seeds chewed when a cold is threatening is a quick way of averting it and the leaves used in salads help tone blood and tissues, aid congested lungs and relieve rheumatic and arthritic pains. Use a handful of chopped leaves in 250 ml (1 cup) boiling water, allow to stand for 10 minutes, then drink for flatulence, pneumonia, colds and catarrh.

Externally, crushed, warmed leaves can be used as a rub or poultice for inflammation, aches, sprains and pains, and also for stiffness of the joints. A mustard plaster is a wonderful pain reliever when applied locally. Use a handful of crushed seeds (125 ml or ½ cup), with the same amount of wholewheat flour, mix to a paste with hot water and add 6 ml (½ tbls) vinegar. Spread on a cloth and apply hot over the painful area (I heat the vinegar first). Repeat when necessary.

Mustard must be one of the easiest plants to grow. Even seeds sprinkled on wet cotton wool or lint in a tray and kept wet will sprout and send up delicious little green-topped succulent garnishes in no time at all. Children find it infinitely satisfying as they can watch the seeds actually grow before their eyes.

Dig over a bed and add some manure and compost, about a spadeful of each to a 1 metre square area. Then sow the seed thinly, rake over and water well. Within 10 days the sturdy little green plants will appear. Use the green leaves daily in salads and allow one or two plants to set seed. When these are dry, save some for re-planting and turn the others into herb mustard.

HERB MUSTARD

250 ml (1 cup) mustard seed
10 peppercorns
25 ml (2 tbls) coarse salt
dried lemon peel (half a lemon)
25 ml (2 tbls) honey
12,5–25 ml (1–2 tbls) tarragon vinegar
2 ml (½ tsp) turmeric
5 ml (1 tsp) fresh tarragon, thyme or rosemary, chopped

89

Pound together mustard seed, peppercorns, salt and lemon peel until finely crushed. Mix to a paste with honey and vinegar. Add turmeric and store in well-corked jars. Add a little fresh chopped tarragon, thyme or rosemary. (I take out just enough mustard for the meal, add the chopped herbs and serve. The mustard does not keep well so use it up quickly.)

A delicious mustard sauce can be made from your own crop that will earn you a reputation that will be hard to beat:

MUSTARD SAUCE

2 green peppers
1 red pepper
100 g (4 oz) ripe tomatoes
2 large onions
half a cucumber
50 g (2 oz) pickled cucumbers
1,2 litres (2 pts) water
12,5 ml (1 tbls) salt
570 ml (1 pt) white vinegar
250 g (8 oz) soft brown sugar
25 ml (2 tbls) mustard seed
25 ml (2 tbls) flour
1 ml (¼ tsp) turmeric

Remove pips from green peppers, skin the tomatoes, chop all the vegetables and place in a bowl. Add water and salt, cover and leave overnight in a cool place. Next day strain vegetables, discarding the salt water in which they were soaked, place in a large heavy-bottomed pan, add vinegar, sugar and mustard seed and boil. Mix flour and turmeric and a little water and slowly add to the boiling vegetable mixture, stirring well. Simmer uncovered for 1¼ hours until the sauce has thickened, stirring occasionally. Liquidise for 2–3 minutes then pour into hot sterilised bottles. The yield is about 900 ml (1½ pts). Use as a relish with savoury tarts and meat or chicken dishes. It is also delicious simply spread on toasted sandwiches.

MYRTLE

PLATE 19

Family:	*Myrtaceae*
Species:	*Myrtus communis* (common myrtle)
Plant:	perennial
Height:	up to 3 metres
Soil:	medium rich, well-drained
Exposure:	sun
Propagation:	woody cuttings
Uses:	medicinal, culinary
Meaning:	love

Myrtle is frequently mentioned in the Old Testament and in the works of the ancient Greeks and Romans. It is considered a lucky plant and in several countries is carried by brides in their wedding bouquets. It is also said to be aphrodisiac and is dedicated to Venus, goddess of love. Every part of the plant is highly scented and the leaves and flowers make a beautiful addition to pot-pourris and sachets and are often used in homemade cosmetic recipes.

A brew made from the leaves is soothing for bruises and haemorrhoids. Take 4 handfuls of leaves and flowers, pour over 1 litre (4 cups) boiling water, and allow to stand for an hour. Then dip a cotton cloth in the brew, wring it out and bind it over the bruised area. Apply several times a day to ease the pain. The same brew was once used as a douche for leucorrhoea but has now been replaced by stronger herbs. Its properties are astringent and antiseptic and the same brew is an excellent wash for the face to tighten pores and tone the skin.

Dried flower buds and the berry-like fruit can be crushed and used in place of peppercorns – a most interesting taste. A small handful of leaves sprinkled over roast pork in the final 10 minutes of roasting gives a delicious flavour. Fresh flowers can be added to salads and fruit salads.

A refreshing vinegar to use in the bath can be made by heating 1 litre (4 cups) apple cider vinegar with a large handful of myrtle leaves and flowers, a handful of rosemary twigs and 10 cloves. Bring to the boil, then remove from the stove and allow to steep. Strain off the vinegar and bottle, adding a fresh sprig each of myrtle and rosemary. Two or three tablespoons in your evening bath will do much to soothe aching muscles and combat general fatigue.

To propagate, choose woody twigs in midsummer, pull off with a small heel and strip the lower leaves. Press into a mixture of peat and sand-filled trays. Cover with a plastic tent and keep moist until rooted. Then remove the plastic and allow to establish strongly before planting in compost and soil-filled bags.

Myrtle is slow growing and needs time to get to a size large enough to plant out. Place the bags in a partially shaded position and do not allow to dry out, but take care not to over-water either as myrtle does not like wet feet. Once sturdy and strong, plant out 1–2 metres apart in well-dug holes to which a little compost has been added (one spadeful per shrub). Water well until established and thereafter a weekly watering is all that is necessary. Apart from the occasional trimming, myrtle requires no further attention and will give you much pleasure. (Remember to save all the trimmed off pieces for drying for pot-pourris.)

In the hot dusty months an occasional spray of water will keep its leaves looking their shiny, evergreen best.

NASTURTIUM

PLATE 19

Family:	*Tropaeolaceae*
Species:	*Tropaeolum majus, T. minus*
Plant:	perennial, grown as an annual
Height:	37 cm (trailing); 30 cm
Soil:	sandy
Exposure:	sun
Propagation:	seeds
Uses:	culinary, medicinal
Meaning:	patriotism

Two varieties of the *Tropaeolum* species are most often grown in herb gardens: *Tropaeolum majus*, which has the long, trailing stems and is known as the common nasturtium, and the compact, bushy *Tropaeolum minus*, growing to about 30 cm in height and width.

Medicinally the leaves are used as an antibiotic for blood and digestive ailments. The seeds are used to repel worms, and can also be crushed and applied externally as a poultice to draw abscesses, boils and old sores which have become infected. The leaves and flowers can be eaten in salads and are a wonderful cure for depression, nervous anxiety and tiredness, and are also said to improve poor eyesight. A known relief and cure for a sore throat is to eat 3 nasturtium leaves to start with, then 2 more at intervals of 3 hours.

The hot biting taste of the nasturtium makes a delicious base for a Worcestershire-type sauce, which can be stored and used for a flavouring that is hard to beat.

NASTURTIUM SAUCE

570 ml (1 pt) dark vinegar
3 garlic cloves
6 whole cloves
5 ml (1 tsp) salt
2 ml (½ tsp) cayenne pepper
1 chopped onion
5 cups nasturtium flowers, fairly loosely packed

Boil up the vinegar, onion and other ingredients and pour over the nasturtium flowers which have been placed in a consul preserving jar. Screw on lid while still hot. Leave for about 2 months, then strain and add 250 ml (1 cup) soy sauce. Stir well and bottle in attractive bottles. It keeps well and can be used like Worcestershire sauce added to soups and savoury dishes.

Sow seeds in spring 40 cm apart where they are to flower and keep damp. I usually cover them with a fairly thick layer of leaves and grass to keep the soil from drying out. In frost-free areas nasturtiums can be perennial, self-seeding and abundant.

Nasturtiums seem to thrive in most soil types, but do best in sandy soil. When preparing a bed for nasturtiums dig in a generous amount of well-rotted manure and compost and sow the seeds in moist, friable soil. Keep well watered until mature and then water once a week. Pick the flowers often.

NETTLE

PLATE 20

Family:	*Urticaceae*
Species:	*Urtica dioica*
Plant:	perennial
Height:	up to 120 cm
Soil:	not fussy
Exposure:	sun
Propagation:	seeds, division
Uses:	medicinal, culinary
Meaning:	slander

Once you have been stung by a nettle you will not easily forget the plant! It is the formic acid in the leaves which causes the painful stinging and blisters.

The nettle has for many centuries been used in the manufacture of cloth, as a food and medicinally (during Roman times nettle branches were used to flog the limbs of rheumatism sufferers!). It is a diuretic, a laxative, a great aid in skin conditions such as eczema, and it lowers the blood sugar level.

The root is used in the treatment of lymphatic ailments and to expel gallstones and kidney stones. The leaves can be lightly cooked and eaten as a vegetable served with butter, salt and pepper and a squeeze of lemon juice. This is also a wonderful blood tonic and cleanser and will aid anaemia, rheumatism, sciatica, arthritis, obesity and infertility.

A tea made from the leaf will aid excessive menstrual flow and internal haemor-rhaging and will also tone the blood and tissues. Add 250 ml (1 cup) leaves to 500 ml (2 cups) boiling water, stand, then strain and drink 125 ml (½ cup) three times a day. Alternatively, 250 ml (1 cup) nettle flowers, heated gently in 500 ml (2 cups) wine, will be as effective; the dose is one wineglassful drunk daily.

Nettles used as a hair wash, rinse and scalp massage will tone the scalp and re-move dandruff. Take one large handful of nettle tops (wear gloves when picking them!) and pour 1 litre (4 cups) water over them. Allow to steep for 10 minutes, then pour the liquid off and use as a scalp lotion.

Propagation is by seed, which needs to be collected in the wild, or by root div-ision. Cut the plant back before attempting to dig it out. Then, using gloves at all times, separate pieces of stem with roots attached and plant these in a dug-over bed with a little manure added to it, spacing them 60 cm apart. Water well and do not al-low to dry out until established. Cut back once a year to encourage compact growth. Separate the plants in spring if the area becomes too crowded.

Be sure you plant the nettles in an out of the way spot of the garden so that they are not easily rubbed against. In case you do get stung it is a good idea to have a dock plant, some plaintain or mint growing nearby to rub onto the stung area for instant relief.

OREGANUM

PLATE 18

Family:	*Labiatae*
Species:	*Origanum vulgare*
Plant:	perennial
Height:	60–75 cm
Soil:	average
Exposure:	sun
Propagation:	seeds, cuttings
Uses:	culinary, medicinal
Meaning:	blushes

Oreganum is also known as wild marjoram and it is closely related to marjoram, often a cause of confusion to the uninitiated. The creeping type of oreganum has pinkish flowers and the bush type has small white flowers. The leaves have a stronger and more pungent flavour than marjoram and can be used fresh or dried (oregano). The plant withstands frost and also makes a good container plant. It does need sun, however, so be sure to stand it on a sunny windowsill.

There is a legend which tells how oreganum got its name: once upon a time Oregano, a young servant of King Cinyras of Crete, was carrying a large vessel full of a valuable perfume of which the king was particularly fond. He tripped and dropped the vessel, spilling the precious liquid. In his shock and anguish and fear of punishment, he fainted and while lying on the ground was metamorphosed into the fragrant oreganum plant, absorbing some of the fragrance of the spilled perfume.

Oreganum is good for indigestion and for breaking up fatty food in the stomach. A tea using a thumb-length piece of oreganum in 250 ml (1 cup) boiling water, will ease coughing, bronchitis and colic. Where an antiseptic is needed, a handful of oreganum tied in a muslin bag can be used in a hot bath. Chew a fresh piece to help indigestion.

Oreganum is a delicious culinary herb and particularly enhances tomato and pasta dishes. Because of its wonderful medicinal uses perhaps it should be included in more dishes and experimentation could be exciting.

OREGANO MACARONI

2 cups wholewheat macaroni pieces
1 large onion, chopped
37,5 ml (3 tbls) butter
5 ml (1 tsp) salt
12,5 ml (1 tbls) flour
1 green pepper cut into 4 pieces
10 ml (2 tsp) fresh oreganum, chopped
10 ml (2 tsp) parsley, chopped
12,5 ml (1 tbls) tomato paste
250 ml (1 cup) sour cream

Sauté onion in butter. Add salt, green pepper, oreganum and parsley. Cover and cook slowly for 10 minutes. Remove the green pepper. Sprinkle in the flour. Stir in tomato paste. Add sour cream.

Meanwhile cook macaroni pieces in salted boiling water until tender. Drain, arrange in a hot serving dish and pour sauce over it. Bon appetit!

I have found oreganum seed slow to germinate and, as cuttings are so easy to root, it seems that this is the quickest way to propagate. Cuttings can be taken at any time of the year and pressed into wet sand. Keep moist and shaded. Harden off by standing the tray in the sun for some days before transplanting. Plant out into the garden when well rooted. Water twice weekly and leave 30–50 cm between plants as they spread quickly.

Flowers should be kept cut back to encourage leaf growth and bushiness or the plant becomes too straggly and untidy. The creeping variety spreads by runners and these root easily so can be cut away and replanted in another position.

PARSLEY

Family: *Umbelliferae*
Species: *Petroselinum crispum*
Plant: biennial
Height: 15–25 cm
Soil: moist, moderately rich
Exposure: partial shade, sun
Propagation: seeds
Uses: culinary, medicinal

There are several varieties of parsley, not only the moss-curled *Petroselinum crispum*, and no herb garden should ever be without it. It is so filled with goodness that it can be added to any dish, and it clears and sweetens the breath of garlic and onion odours. In cooking, always add parsley at the last possible moment as cooking spoils it and takes the goodness from it.

Parsley seeds germinate slowly and as several nurseries offer small seedlings, if you are impatient it will save time if you start with these. If not, in early spring sow seed that has been soaked in warm (not hot) water in a thermos overnight into sand-filled trays. Soak the tray in water and then cover finely with sand. Place a sheet of glass over the tray and keep in the shade. Once the seed has sprouted the glass can be removed and the trays kept moist. Transplant 15–20 cm apart when you can handle the plants and keep shaded with hessian or cloches for a few days. Parsley needs semi-filtered shade to really do well in South Africa, or morning sun and afternoon shade. Keep the soil fairly moist and dig in a lot of compost throughout the summer.

Parsley is a biennial and the flowering period can be postponed by picking the leaves often and cutting down the flowering stems.

Parsley dries beautifully and can be used in bouquet garnis and for flavouring. Do try to have it growing continuously in the garden, however, as fresh chopped parsley does add a special touch to any dish. Parsley also makes a charming border to a rose bed and is a wonderful companion plant.

1

2

3

1 Mustard *p 89*
2 Myrtle *p 91*
3 Nasturtium *p 93*

1

3

2

4

1 Nettle *p 95*
2 Parsley *p 98*
3 Pennyroyal *p 99*
4 Periwinkle *p 100*

1 Cotyledon (pig's ear) *p 47*
2 Prickly pear *p 101*
3 Pumpkin *p 102*

1

2

1 Pyrethrum *p 104*
2 Quince *p 105*

PENNYROYAL

PLATE 20

Family: *Labiatae*
Species: *Mentha pulegium*
Plant: creeping perennial
Height: ground cover
Soil: any, prefers light, well-drained
Exposure: sun, partial shade
Propagation: runners
Uses: medicinal, fragrance
Meaning: flee

Pennyroyal belongs to the mint family but because of its wonderful medicinal properties and its different growth pattern to its close relatives, it needs separate treatment. It makes an excellent ground cover – in less than 6 months it can cover a large area. Like the other mints, it too creeps ever onward, searching for new ground, so it needs to be checked and cut back. These cut pieces can be replanted in a dug over, well-manured bed, spacing them 15 cm apart. The centre of the old plants will die out, so it is good to be able to replace them with new rooted pieces. Pennyroyal is also a beautiful container plant and is attractive in a window-box or hanging basket as it will hang over the sides. In midsummer it produces 15 cm long stems of lilac flowers in whorls, which can be dried, as can the leaves, for a fresh fragrance in potpourris.

Pennyroyal is an effective insecticide and when rubbed onto the skin will repel most insects. Dried pennyroyal sprinkled around and in ants' nests will deter them too. Fresh pennyroyal rubbed onto dogs' coats will prove how its other name, 'fleabane', was earned; a few fresh sprays in their baskets, replaced daily, will keep their bedding flea and tick free. A fresh sprig rubbed along window-sills and counter-tops in the kitchen quickly sends the flies out.

Medicinally it is used for bronchial and chest ailments, and when the fragrance from the crushed leaves is inhaled, it clears the sinuses and a stuffed nose. When used medicinally, however, it is essential that this is done under the supervision of a homoeopathic doctor or herbalist as *it is a very strong herb and can cause kidney damage* if used too often.

A good twice weekly watering is needed to keep pennyroyal lush and vigorous. It can happily be walked on, and a small fragrant lawn in the centre of the herb garden is a charming and different idea. Each season dig some old manure and compost into the bed around the plants. Rooted cuttings can be started in August to fill in where old plants have died before the summer's growth. Just take a sand-filled tray, press the cutting well into it and keep moist. Pennyroyal is an easy plant to grow and will give much pleasure.

PERIWINKLE

PLATE 20

Family:	*Apocynaceae*
Species:	*Vinca major, V. minor*
Plant:	perennial
Height:	trailing ground cover
Soil:	any, poor
Exposure:	sun, partial shade
Propagation:	rooted stems
Uses:	medicinal, ground cover
Meaning:	friendship

Periwinkle deserves a place in the herb garden as it is a wonderful wound dressing. It stops bleeding – external and internal, including nose-bleeds and excessive menstruation – and dries ulcers, wounds and sores. It is an excellent treatment for chronic diarrhoea and for breast-feeding mothers who have an excessive milk flow or dripping or leaking nipples. Use 1 large handful of leaves and flowers to 500 ml (2 cups) boiling water. Sweeten with honey and take 25 ml (2 tbls) night and morning. To wash wounds and as an external application apply liberally, or soak cotton bandages in the brew and bind over the affected area. For nose-bleeds plug the nose with cotton wool which has been soaked in this brew.

Handfuls of flowers placed in a bowl of rainwater and left in the sun all day make a beautiful astringent face rinse. Keep bottled in the fridge. (Float enough flowers to cover the surface of a fairly shallow bowl.) To make it stronger, cover overnight and in the morning replace those flowers with fresh ones, repeating the sunlight dose.

Vinca is an attractive ground cover but can become unruly if not controlled. Stems root down easily and these can be dug out and replanted about 45 cm apart. The new rooted stems planted into a freshly dug site need to be kept shaded and moist until they have established themselves. I have found that a flat stone, laid on top of the root and stem, gives adequate shade and protection, and they seem to establish very quickly. The stone keeps the soil cool and damp (do not cover the entire plant) and sturdy new shoots will show themselves within a few days. Dig in a dressing of compost from time to time to ensure lush and attractive plants.

Vinca makes a good hanging basket plant, too, and trails beautifully up or down; in a basket, however, it does need compost constantly and frequent watering.

PRICKLY PEAR

PLATE 21

Family:	*Cactaceae*
Species:	*Opuntia vulgaris*
Plant:	perennial
Height:	up to 3,5 metres
Soil:	poor
Exposure:	sun
Propagation:	leaf
Uses:	landscape, medicinal, culinary
Meaning:	satire

Prickly pear deserves a place in the herb garden as it has wonderful and varied medicinal properties. It is a proven remedy for diabetes, whooping cough and sores. It is also an excellent famine food as it requires very little water. You can grow it in any soil merely by placing a leaf on the soil, or by planting the end of a leaf that has been cut off into the soil and pressing down well around it. Water well and it will soon send down roots. The only maintenance required is to chop off leaves now and then if it gets too prolific. It needs to be planted at the back of the garden or in an out-of-the-way corner as it is a quick grower and grows to enormous proportions.

The prickly pear fruit is a bonus which ripens in midsummer. A delicious preserve can be made from it.

Should the plant become infested with the cochineal bug, any of the plant sprays discussed in Chapter 9 will help get rid of it. Alternatively, spray paraffin onto the bugs and, once they have dropped off, hose down with a strong jet of water to clean the leaves. Cochineal bug is very hardy and if even the smallest speck is left it will start up again so either chop off and burn the infected leaf, or spray for 3 days in a row.

Watch out for the tiny thorns when handling the leaves and fruit and save any trimmed off leaves. If you are plagued by mosquitoes and have a stagnant pool nearby filled with mosquito larvae, chop the leaves roughly and toss them into the water where the oil will suffocate the larvae as it floats on the surface.

Prickly pears make a delicious dessert to end a summer supper.

PRICKLY PEAR DESSERT

prickly pears, sliced
mint leaves
white sugar
iced water

Chop mint leaves finely and add the same quantity of white sugar. Mix well, add just a little iced water to make the chopped leaves and sugar stick together, and sprinkle liberally over the prickly pears. Serve chilled, topped with whipped cream.

PUMPKIN

PLATE 21

Family: *Cucurbitaceae*
Species: *Cucurbita maxima*
Plant: annual
Height: creeper up to 60 cm, in length up to 6 metres
Soil: rich, fairly well-drained
Exposure: full sun
Propagation: seeds
Uses: culinary, medicinal
Meaning: thanksgiving

The pumpkin flower, fruit and seeds are all medicinal and the old *boer pampoen* has its own place in South Africa's history. It was brought to South Africa by the French Huguenots and, because it kept so well, the trekkers would take it with them into the interior. It also grew easily from seed and pumpkin soon became an indispensable part of their diet.

Pumpkin flowers are edible and are delicious stuffed with savoury rice and lightly roasted or baked. Pumpkin itself is rich in minerals and vitamins and is very tasty. Bruised pumpkin leaves will repel flies.

The flowers also make a reviving tea (8 flowers to 600 ml (1 pt) boiling water) which strengthens the blood and is of benefit to anaemia and rickets sufferers. The tea is soothing to delicate stomachs. Hot roasted pumpkin is a wonderful drawing poultice for abscesses and boils. Cut the outer skin away and apply the hot flesh to the affected area, taking care not to burn it, and bind in place.

The most beneficial way to eat pumpkin is raw and finely grated. It is not very palatable but, mixed with grated carrot, a squeeze of orange juice and a little grated apple, it is quite pleasant. In cases of anaemia and rickets it should be eaten raw daily in addition to a good helping of either roasted or boiled pumpkin.

Dry a sizeable quantity of pumpkin seeds in the sun, or roast them on a baking tray. Sprinkle lightly with salt and a little water and roast gently for 2 hours. Store them in screw-top bottles for use throughout the year.

To expel worms or to prevent worm infestation, eat 7 pumpkin pips on an empty stomach first thing in the morning for 10 days, chewing them well. To expel tapeworms make a mixture of 12,5 ml (1 tbls) castor oil, 25 ml (2 tbls) crushed, well-dried pumpkin seeds, and 12,5 ml (1 tbls) honey. Fast for a day, taking only fruit juices and the following day, first thing in the morning and on an empty stomach, drink the mixture mixed with a little milk. After 1½ hours drink a purging mixture of 12,5 ml (1 tbls) castor oil, 12,5 ml (1 tbls) honey mixed into 125 ml (½ cup) lemon juice and diluted with a little tepid water. The patient should remain in bed until the purge has worked and eat only oats and skimmed milk for the rest of that and the following day. Be sure that the head of the tapeworm has been expelled.

To grow pumpkins is one of the easiest and most rewarding pleasures. In September dig over a small area well, add a spadeful of old manure, and dig in and water well. Press into the soil a circle of about 5 pumpkin pips spaced 20 cm apart, cover with grass and leaves as a mulch, and keep moist. Soon the bright green leaves of the sprouting seeds will appear. Water regularly and keep the trailing vines tidy by positioning them where you wish them to trail, using confining sticks pressed into the soil. Use herb insect repellents to deter the pumpkin fly. Make small nests of khakibos to hold the ripening fruit – this prevents rot and deters ants and will keep the fruit unblemished.

Sow the seeds in the early spring to save the infestation of insects in the late summer. Regular watering and a spadeful of rich compost lightly dug in around the roots will ensure a satisfying pumpkin crop. Pick when the stems look dry and brittle and store on racks in a cool shed for winter use.

103

PYRETHRUM

PLATE 22

Family: *Compositae*
Species: *Chrysanthemum cinerarifolium*
Plant: perennial
Height: up to 45 cm
Soil: light, well-drained
Exposure: sun
Propagation: seeds
Uses: insecticide

Pyrethrum is one of nature's insecticides and is an attractive garden plant too. Its bright summer daisy-like flower is beautiful in the vase and it lasts well. It is the dried flower-head which is the source of the insecticide, and used in pot-pourris it is an added bonus, as it is both attractive and will keep insects away.

A muslin bag filled with leaves and flowers and hung on a dog's basket will help repel ticks and fleas. Replace with fresh flowers and leaves from time to time. Pyrethrum is toxic to insects but non-toxic to mammals so it can be used liberally. Use crushed flowers and leaves to sprinkle on stored fruit and vegetables and in grain bags and add to cement sprays to spray the walls of storehouses to control pests.

Sow seed in sand-filled trays, cover with a fine layer of sand and keep moist. When the seedlings are big enough to handle transplant into a well-dug bed to which some river sand has been added as the plants need to be in light, well-drained soil. Space 30 cm apart and keep well watered in the early days. Once the plant is growing well water every 2 or 3 days as the soil is quickly drained and it does not retain moisture for long.

After the summer flowering cut back the flowering stalks. Pyrethrum benefits from a mulch of leaves and grass to retain moisture once it has established itself, particularly if grown in a very hot area.

Seed can also be sown where it is to grow and thinned out once it germinates. Be sure to keep the seed bed shaded and moist, using hessian to cover it, supported by sticks, and keep the sides enclosed too as wind dries out the sandy soil. The thinned out plants can be placed elsewhere for when it is young pyrethrum transplants well.

QUINCE

PLATE 22

Family:	*Rosaceae*
Species:	*Cydonia oblonga (Pyrus cydonia)*
Plant:	deciduous shrub
Height:	up to 3,5 metres
Soil:	fairly rich, well-drained
Exposure:	full sun
Propagation:	cuttings
Uses:	medicinal, culinary
Meaning:	temptation

Having a quince shrub in the herb garden is a great asset for not only is it most attractive, but it also has many uses, culinary and medicinal.

The grated raw fruit is an effective cure for diarrhoea – one fruit in the morning and one at night. This can be flavoured with a little lemon juice and honey and, for those who do not like the coarseness of the fruit, it can also be cooked gently in a little water until soft, then mashed or pushed through a sieve. A quick relief for a stomach-ache and colic is 5 ml (1 tsp) quince juice mixed with 2 ml (½ tsp) powdered cloves, taken every few hours.

A wonderful hair tonic can be made from the peel and core of the fruit, and should be massaged into the scalp once a week. Fill half a bucket with quince peels and cores. Fill to the top with water and boil for half an hour. Allow to cool, then strain. This brew is also used for grooming the manes and tails of Arabian thoroughbred horses.

A standard brew, made by boiling 250 ml (1 cup) sliced fruit in 750 ml (3 cups) water, is a soothing cleanser for all discharges of the body, including cysts of the eye, styes, inflammation and ulcers of the eyes. It is also a soothing gargle for mouth ulcers and sore throats and was once used by singers to strengthen their voices.

In August chop off a piece of rooted stem from the cluster of stems that make up the main trunk of the shrub. Place in a deep hole, cover with soil and keep well watered until it sends out new leaves. Then lightly dig in a spade of compost around it and later in the month a spade of old manure. Water well once a week and at the end of summer you will be rewarded with fruit that can be stewed, bottled, jellied and enjoyed. Use a minimal amount of sugar when bottling and keep as a winter medicine. You can also freeze sliced, blanched fruit.

QUINCE JELLY (yields approximately 1,2 kg or 2½ lb)

1,75 kg (4 lb) ripe quinces, sliced
600 ml (1 pt) water
6 allspice berries, bruised
lemon juice
sugar

Boil quinces, allspice berries and the water for 50 minutes or until the fruit is soft, keeping covered all the while. Pour the pulp into a jelly bag or bag made up of half a metre of butter muslin sewn up on 3 sides. Suspend this from a cup-hook or tap with a bowl beneath it to catch the juice and let it drip overnight. Discard the remaining pulp, measure the juice and return to the rinsed pot. To every 600 ml (1 pt) juice add 12,5 ml (1 tbls) lemon juice and 400 g (14 oz) sugar. Place over low heat and stir well until the sugar is dissolved, then boil briskly for 10 minutes or until the jelly reaches setting point. Skim the foam off the surface and ladle jelly into hot jars. Cover with a piece of greaseproof paper soaked in brandy. Screw on tops and label. Store in a cool pantry. Serve as a jam or with meat dishes, curries or desserts.

RADISH

Family: *Cruciferae*
Species: *Raphanus sativus*
Plant: annual
Height: up to 15 cm
Soil: friable, rich
Exposure: sun
Propagation: seeds
Uses: medicinal, culinary

This well-known salad vegetable has been cultivated for so long that its origin is uncertain. It probably originated in China where many varieties of the radish are still grown today.

The black radish varieties are used in homoeopathic medicine and some seed catalogues offer the seeds in their vegetable sections.

The medicinal properties of the lowly radish are many and varied – antibiotic, tonic, carminative, choleretic and nutritive. When one considers how easy they are to grow almost all through the year it seems a shame that neat rows of radishes are not found in more gardens.

Virtually all of the plant is used: leaves, root, juice from the root and the young seed pods. Chopped fresh root gives relief from dyspepsia and is used to promote salivation.

A few radishes should be included in the daily diet. They are delicious sliced on brown bread with a little salt and the young seed pods can be added to relishes and pickles. Radishes are rich in vitamin C and, chopped finely, should be added to dishes in times of infection or illness as they are a natural antibiotic. Alternatively the leaves and finely shaved or grated root – 12,5 ml (1 tbls) to 250 ml (1 cup) boiling water – can be drunk during the day or, if eating is not easy during the illness, a table-spoon at a time is as effective.

To plant, make shallow drills with a rake in well-dug, rich soil, sprinkle the seed thinly in the drill, rake over the soil and keep well watered until the seeds are up. In the hot summer months shade with grass or mulch with leaves and veld grass until the seeds germinate. Sow a successive crop every three weeks and enjoy this sparkling, crisp, natural tonic. Use the leaves in soups and stews. Each time you sow radish seeds be sure to dig in 4–6 spadefuls of compost per square metre as they are voracious feeders and quickly use up the soil's nourishment. The more thinly you space the seeds, the bigger the individual plant will be. Approximately 30–40 cm apart is ideal.

RHUBARB

PLATE 23

Family:	*Polygonaceae*
Species:	*Rheum rhaponticum*
Plant:	perennial
Height:	up to 60 cm
Soil:	rich, moist
Exposure:	sun
Propagation:	seed, root division
Uses:	culinary, medicinal
Meaning:	advice

Garden rhubarb is an old favourite for rhubarb pie and rhubarb crumble but it has medicinal properties, too, which should ensure it a place in every herb garden. *The leaves have a very high oxalic acid content and are poisonous.*

Rhubarb stems, stewed with a little sugar, act as a gentle laxative and the dried and powdered root mixed with water to make a paste is a light yellow hair dye. Because of their high acidic content crushed leaves can be used to scour copper and brass; combined with salt and lemon juice, this is a magical cleaner for any items which are badly tarnished. Boil up a crushed leaf in a kettle to descale it if the water is hard as the acid breaks down the furriness.

The dried and powdered root (use a pestle and mortar) is an astringent stomach and bowel medicine and is a beneficial treatment for acne. Use 5 ml (1 tsp) to 1 litre (4 cups) water and drink three times a day to ease gripes and diarrhoea. The same brew can be used 2 or 3 times a day for treating acne.

There are several species of rhubarb, some of which were used in China as long ago as 3000 BC. Some have a stronger action than garden rhubarb so handle with caution and do not take internally unless under a doctor's supervision.

Rhubarb can be grown from seed in damp sand with just enough sand to cover the seed. Keep shaded and moist until they are well established. Plant out into the garden when big enough to handle, 60 cm apart, and shade until sturdy. Then give them a deep watering once a week, mulching with compost and well-rotted manure.

Easier by far is to take root cuttings. Choose pieces of root, each with a bud or eye on it, and plant into rich, well-manured soil. The soil must be deeply forked, at least 45 cm in depth, and should have plenty of old, well-rotted manure dug into it. The stalks should not be pulled in the first year and in subsequent years pick only until midsummer to ensure healthy productive crowns. Each spring lightly dig in a spadeful or two of manure and compost around each crown. Water deeply once a week throughout spring and summer. In winter water only occasionally. Lift and divide established crowns in July or early August so that they can re-establish themselves before spring. Plant the crowns 60 cm apart.

ROCK ROSE

PLATE 23

Family:	*Cistaceae*
Species:	*Cistus villosus*
Plant:	perennial
Height:	up to 90 cm
Soil:	poor, well-drained
Exposure:	sun
Propagation:	cuttings
Uses:	medicinal, cosmetic

The rock rose is a surprisingly wonderful herb and it is a calming, soothing remedy for many ills. It can be used as a gargle for sore throats and as a wash to treat venereal diseases. Taken as a standard brew – 5 flowers and 5 leaves to 250 ml (1 cup) boiling water – 25 ml (2 tbls) taken 3 times a day will relax, calm and give courage and confidence to an anxious child.

The sticky substance contained in the leaves is the oil of labdanum which is a perfume fixative. It is commercially harvested in Crete and Cyprus by sweeping the bushes with leather-thonged combs. Angora goats are sent to graze in amongst the rock rose bushes and each evening their beards are combed to remove the sticky oil! The oily substance is then scraped off, formed into cakes and sun dried. Little wonder that its price is so high for only a small amount can be gleaned from a combing.

Cistus villosus is not fussy where it grows and needs little water. Cuttings can be taken at any time of the year if they can be kept warm and protected. Press the cuttings into wet sand and keep covered with plastic. Check daily and keep moist. Harden off by removing the covering once they have rooted and gradually giving them a little sunlight, lengthening the time each day. Plant out into plastic bags large enough to enable them to grow undisturbed for some months. Plant in the garden 90 cm from each other and water well; thereafter only water when they dry out. Rock rose dislikes wet feet – perhaps that is why it enjoys growing in a rockery.

Apart from an occasional trimming, rock rose needs very little attention and its rosy flowers will give pleasure all summer long.

ROSE

Family:	*Rosaceae*
Species:	*Rosa*
Plant:	perennial shrub
Height:	up to 3 metres
Soil:	average
Exposure:	sun
Propagation:	cuttings
Uses:	fragrance, landscape, medicinal
Meaning:	love

The rose belongs in every herb garden for its fragrance, its beauty and its medicinal properties. In the old herb gardens it was the cabbage rose, *R. centifolia*, which pre-dominated, and which subsequently went out of fashion. Now there are nurseries which have begun to stock the old roses again so we can once more delight in their age-old beauty in our own gardens.

Choosing varieties is a matter of personal preference, but my favourite is 'Crimson Glory' as it makes the most beautiful rosewater which can be used in many ways. Rose petal tea with honey is a calming, tranquillising, sleep-inducing tea and crystallized rose petals (with the bitter white heel removed) are a delicate, attractive confectionery.

CRYSTALLIZED ROSE PETALS

castor sugar
white of one egg
fresh rose petals

Check that each petal is not dew wet and choose firm, different coloured petals. Whisk the egg white with a fork until it is opaque but not foaming and dip each petal into it or paint with a small pastry brush. Sprinkle well with castor sugar, making sure that the petals are thoroughly coated. Lay each petal on greaseproof paper on a wire rack, cover with another sheet to protect from dust and dry in a very low oven overnight with the door left ajar. Store in air-tight jars and use for cake and pudding decorations.

When planting roses, dig a hole 60 cm wide and 45 cm deep. Make a mound in the centre and stand the rose on it, spreading out its roots. Cover with soil, press well down and water liberally. Rose planting is usually done in July, as is the pruning. Do not put manure or compost into the hole but rather, once it is established, mulch with coarse compost and water weekly. If you choose climbers see that their supports are in position before planting or you may damage the roots if you dig holes afterwards for trellises or poles.

Roses do need to be pruned and old blooms cut off. During the summer months they need to be sprayed with a weak solution of Jeyes Fluid or the spray for roses in

110

Chapter 9 for black spot, red spider and aphids. An observant eye watching for the destructive rose beetle is essential.

Propagation can be done by taking cuttings from a strong flowering stem just as the bloom has faded. Cut off the rose flower and cut the stem into lengths with 3 or 4 eyes on each piece. Press halfway into wet sand and keep watered and cool until new shoots appear. Then strengthen by exposing to a little sun for longer periods each day and plant out into bags to become well established before planting in the garden, approximately 120 cm apart. For the most attractive display plant three or four roses of the same variety in a group or as a feature in a bed.

Use the dried petals in pot-pourris and in rose petal conserve and ice-cream.

ROSEMARY

PLATE 24

Family: *Labiatae*
Species: *Rosmarinus officinalis*
Plant: perennial
Height: 60 cm–1,8 m
Soil: dry, sandy, poor
Exposure: full sun
Propagation: cuttings
Uses: culinary, medicinal, insecticide
Meaning: remembrance

Rosemary is one of the most beautiful and most necessary herbs in any garden. It has long been regarded as a sacred herb and there are many legends surrounding the beautiful blue colour of the flowers. One belief was that the Virgin Mary, on her flight into Egypt, threw her blue cloak over a rosemary bush to dry after washing it. Another version was that she sought cover behind a rosemary bush along the roadside to avoid being found by her persecutors.

Rosemary can be used to make a tea as well as an effective hair lotion. The tea is made using one thumb-length sprig of rosemary and pouring over 250 ml (1 cup) boiling water. Squeeze a little lemon juice into it and sweeten with honey. A rosemary bush planted in each corner of the garden will keep away evil spirits too!

Culinary and medicinal uses abound. Rosemary is a delicious flavouring for lamb, as well as bean and tomato dishes. Use it sparingly, however, as it has a strong flavour and too much can spoil a dish rather than enhance it.

Medicinally it is used for jaundice, migraine, as a general heart tonic and, steeped in wine, it is an excellent pick-me-up. The standard brew is one thumb-length sprig in 250 ml (1 cup) boiling water. Steep, then strain and drink 2 or 3 times daily. To make rosemary wine push 4–6 thumb-length sprigs into a bottle of good red wine. Stand it in the sun for a week, then strain and re-bottle the wine, adding one fresh rosemary sprig. Label and sip a tablespoon twice a day as a tonic. Combined with beer rosemary is also a useful insecticide: use 5 ml (1 tsp) rosemary oil to 300 ml (1¼ cups) beer, mix, steep overnight and spray onto ailing plants.

A cutting taken with a small heel is a quick rooter and rosemary does well in all sorts of soils, although it seems to prefer sandy, light soil. It does not need too much water and really requires so little attention that it is the most worthwhile of all plants to grow.

It responds well to container culture – but bear in mind that it needs a large pot as it grows comparatively quickly and has a large root system.

RUE

PLATE 24

Family: *Rutaceae*
Species: *Ruta graveolens*
Plant: perennial
Height: up to 90 cm
Soil: slightly alkaline, average
Exposure: sun
Propagation: seeds, cuttings
Uses: medicinal, insecticide
Meaning: disdain

The word 'rue' means 'sorrow' or 'pity' and the leaves were once added to holy water used to bless sinners. In some oriental countries rue is grown to protect the household against all kinds of evil.

Take care with rue as it can cause a skin rash if handled during certain times of the year, while at other times it seems harmless. This allergic reaction usually occurs in hot weather.

Rue's medicinal uses are so varied it is difficult to believe that they are all contained in one plant. Rue leaf and honey is good for respiratory and heart ailments. A rue lotion is an excellent drawing poultice for abscesses and boils and a rue decoction can be taken to relieve tiredness and anxiety. Because it is such a strong herb the dosage must be small – five ml (1 tsp) chopped leaves to 500 ml (2 cups) boiling water, steeped for 20 minutes. Strain and take a small wineglassful twice daily for menstrual pain, heart palpitations, epilepsy, fevers, colic, worms, the treatment of rabies, upset stomach, ringworm, convulsions in children, snakebite, and externally for skin parasites, lice and eye ailments! Bunches of rue hung in the house will help keep flies and mosquitoes away, while bunches of leaves tied in a muslin bag and put in the bathwater will help prevent convulsions. Even a rolled-up, bruised leaf will soothe an aching tooth.

Don't plant rue near basil as one or the other will die. Always use rue with care and consult a homoeopathic doctor or registered herbalist before treating yourself.

Cuttings can be taken at any time of the year. Choose small, strong side shoots and press into wet sand. Keep moist until well rooted. Seed germinates if it is really fresh but be patient as I have found germination is sporadic. Rue is unfussy as far as soil type is concerned but it does not like its feet wet and does not grow well in acid soil. It also needs full sun and must be trimmed back from time to time. Keep all the trimmed pieces and dry to use as an insecticide, sprinkling on insect infested plants and around the base of plants to deter ants.

Plant new rue plants 50–60 cm apart in a well-prepared bed. The roots go deep so make sure your holes are fairly deep to ensure that you have an attractive bush, otherwise rue tends to become straggly.

SAGE

Family:	*Labiatae*
Species:	*Salvia officinalis, S. sclarea* (clary), *S. gracilistyle,*
	S. elegans (pineapple sage), *S. variegata*
	(golden sage), *S. purpurescens* (purple-leaved)
Plant:	perennial
Height:	30–45 cm
Soil:	poor, dry, well-drained
Exposure:	full sun
Propagation:	cuttings, seed (if fresh)
Uses:	culinary, medicinal
Meaning:	domestic virtue

Sage has such a variation of uses that it is one of the most essential herbs to grow in the garden or window-box.

In the sixteenth century sage was so highly esteemed that it was said of it: 'Why should a man die whilst sage grows in his garden?' There are varieties of sage which are attractive, and all have medicinal uses. A bed of different varieties can make an interesting corner in the herb garden.

A close relative is clary sage or *Salvia sclarea*, a biennial, once used to treat eye infections, which is a valuable asset in the garden because the leaves are edible; they can be fried in batter like comfrey leaves and eaten with lamb dishes. Clary grows tall so keep it to the back of the bed. It does best in partial shade or shade in the afternoon.

Clary is a lovely cut flower, particularly for old-fashioned mixed bowls. Place the stems in boiling water for a few minutes after cutting them, then add a dessertspoon of sugar to the bowl of water as you arrange the flowers. The leaves can be dried and crumbled and used as a fixative in pot-pourris; the dried flowers are useful in pot-pourris too. Clary sage seeds itself well and once it is happily established in the garden you need never worry to sow seeds again.

Pineapple sage (*Salvia gracilistyle* or *Salvia elegans*) is tall, bushy and fruit-scented and needs a large space, preferably behind the other sages. It will reach 90 cm if planted in nourishing soil and does well with compost around it. It is frost tender and I have saved it from total winter extinction in the heavy frost belt by cutting back in late autumn just before the frost and covering with grass and leaves. In spring, when all danger of frost is past, the leaf and grass blanket can be removed and new shoots quickly appear.

The red flowers of pineapple sage attract bees and red is one of the rarer colours in the herb garden where soft greens, greys, mauves and blues predominate, denoting the healing, restful properties. Dried leaves and flowers are beautiful in pot-pourris.

A most delicious summer punch can be made using pineapple sage and it is a party favourite.

2

1

Joan van Gogh

1 Rhubarb *p 108*
2 Rock rose *p 109*

1
2

1 Rosemary *p 112*
2 Rue *p 113*

2

3

1

1 Cotton lavender (santolina) *p 46*
2 Sage *p 114*
3 Salad burnet *p 116*

1

2

3

1 Savory *p 117*
2 Soap wort *p 121*
3 Sorrel *p 122*

PINEAPPLE PUNCH

4 large handfuls pineapple sage
4 litres boiling water
2 lemons, squeezed
250 ml (1 cup) honey
2 litres (8 cups) pure pineapple juice
1 pineapple, finely chopped

Pour boiling water over the pineapple sage and leave overnight. Strain and add the rest of the ingredients. Refrigerate and serve with a few fresh leaves of pineapple sage and ice.

There is a golden sage, *Salvia variegata*, which is a smaller, more compact bush, best suited for the foreground, and the purple-leafed variety, *Salvia purpurescens*, grows equally neatly. Both these sage bushes are more finicky, however, and often for no apparent reason turn up their toes and die, something which sage is prone to do.

Sage does not like water sprayed on its leaves, nor does it like water-logged soil or having its roots disturbed by digging too deeply around it. It really is heart-breaking when a beautiful bush suddenly dies but one consolation is that every leaf can be gathered and used – dug back into the soil or put onto the compost heap. Dug in around grapes, it makes an excellent fertilizer.

Cut back the flowering spikes after they fade and keep the bushes trimmed. Cuttings can be taken at any time of the year from garden sage and from pineapple sage, except in the coldest months, and new plants should be kept growing continuously to replace those in the border or herb garden that die. Fresh seed germinates well and quickly and seedlings transplanted when just big enough to handle make excellent pot-plants. Choose a sandy soil mixture and see that there is good drainage in the pots. They should stand in full sun on a patio or balcony and need to be watered only once a week, or twice a week in very hot weather.

Sage tea is extremely beneficial for colds and sore throats; even chewing a sage leaf will ease the ache of a sore throat. Sage tonic is an anti-depressant and a pick-me-up and can be easily made by infusing 10 sage leaves in 500 ml (2 cups) boiling water and leaving to draw. Then add 500 ml (2 cups) claret and bottle with a whole nutmeg and a stick of cinnamon, and keep in the refrigerator. Drink a wineglassful each evening – it can be warmed to drink in winter.

Sage can be dried by hanging it in bunches or laying it on racks in the shade. Crumble and store in glass bottles for winter use. Fresh sage has a much better flavour, however, so try always to have a bush or two in the garden.

SALAD BURNET

PLATE 25

Family: *Rosaceae*
Species: *Sanguisorba officinalis*
Plant: perennial
Height: 20–45 cm
Soil: average, likes moisture
Exposure: sun
Propagation: seeds, division
Uses: culinary, medicinal

As a medicinal herb, salad burnet is useful as a refrigerant (blood cooling), a tonic, for healing wounds and soothing sunburn. Pour 250 ml (1 cup) boiling water onto 8 mature leaf sprays and drink 125 ml (½ cup) morning and night. The same brew can be used for skin ailments as a wash or applied to sunburn and eczema as a lotion. There is a legend which illustrates salad burnet's wound-healing property of supposedly slowing the flow of blood. Apparently King Chaba of Hungary, after a great battle many centuries ago, used it to heal the wounds of 15 000 of his soldiers!

Seeds sown in moist sand germinate readily and you will find the plant seeds itself so prolifically that once you have it in the garden you will never be without it.

It has a fresh cucumber-like flavour and, as it is a tonic herb, it should perhaps be more widely used than it is in salads and soups. Chopped finely and mixed into salad dressings or in cream cheese with celery, it is really delicious, but use only the young new leaves as the older leaves tend to become stringy.

Salad burnet survives winter well and it can be separated as it grows into an untidy bundle if it is not controlled. Basal rosettes spread out to about 30 cm and I find that using new seedlings each season keeps it more attractive, especially if it is used as a border edging plant. Flower-heads should be cut back to encourage new leaf growth from the crown. Use the older leaves for making burnet vinegar as it does not keep its flavour when dried or frozen.

SALAD BURNET VINEGAR

Put a handful of leaves into a bottle of good white vinegar (or cider vinegar if you want to use it for coughs and sore throats). Place in the sun for 10 days, changing the herb for fresh leaves at least three times in that period. Strain and pour into fresh bottles, decorate with a leaf spray or two and label. Use in salad dressings.

SALAD BURNET SOUR CREAM DIP

250 ml (1 cup) young salad burnet leaves, chopped
½ litre (2 cups) sour cream or yoghurt

Mix ingredients together. Flavour with salt and pepper and use as a spread or dip.

SAVORY

There are two savory varieties: summer savory, an annual, and winter savory, a hardy perennial, similar in taste but with different habits.

WINTER SAVORY

Family:	*Labiatae*
Species:	*Satureja montana* (*Satureia montana*)
Plant:	perennial
Height:	30 cm
Soil:	light, well-drained
Exposure:	full sun
Propagation:	cuttings, seeds
Uses:	culinary, medicinal

Winter savory has a lower, more spreading growth than summer savory and makes a good edging to a path in the herb garden. Leaves are used for flavouring bean dishes, and to make a tea for winter coughs and colds, using lemon, honey and hot water.

The whole plant winters well, so there is really no need to dry and store it, except perhaps to add to a bouquet garni mixture.

A wonderful cold and flu recipe which includes winter savory was discovered by two professors of the Montpellier Medical School in France. At the first signs of a cold drink infusions of this herb made by adding to one litre (4 cups) boiling water one cinnamon stick, 10 ml (2 tsp) dried winter savory, or 20 ml (4 tsp) fresh winter savory, and 5 cloves. Boil for exactly 3 minutes. Drink a medium sized glassful morning, noon and night.

Winter savory grows easily from cuttings taken at any time of the year except in the coldest months. It also germinates slowly but fairly well from seed providing the seed is fresh. Plant out 30 cm apart and water well in the first weeks until established. Thereafter water once a week and dig in a little compost around the roots from time to time.

SUMMER SAVORY

Family:	*Labiatae*
Species:	*Satureja hortensis*
Plant:	annual
Height:	30–45 cm
Soil:	light, well-drained
Exposure:	sun
Propagation:	seeds
Uses:	culinary, aromatic

Summer savory can become top heavy as a result of its branching habit, so it is a good idea to support it on a forked twig to prevent it toppling in heavy rain. If it is allowed to set seed it will always keep you supplied with fresh plants.

For winter use cut off the leaves (you will be able to trim back the plant twice in the summer season before the frost comes) and dry on a screen in the shade. Store in glass bottles when dry and add a teaspoon or two to bean and cabbage dishes.

Plant out new seedlings 20–30 cm apart in light well-dug soil, into which 4 spadefuls of compost per square metre have been dug. Keep well watered until sturdy, then water twice a week.

SAVORY VEGETABLE CASSEROLE

450 g (1 lb) broccoli
1 medium-sized cauliflower
500 ml (2 cups) diced green beans
250 ml (1 cup) chicken stock
250 ml (1 cup) sour cream or plain yoghurt
250 ml (1 cup) grated carrot
37,5 ml (3 tbls) chopped chives
1 ml (¼ tsp) lemon pepper
juice of 1 lemon
2 ml (½ tsp) salt
25 ml (2 tbls) chopped summer savory
37,5 ml (3 tbls) fresh brown breadcrumbs
25 ml (2 tbls) flour
grated cheese

Cut up the vegetables. Blend stock, cream, flour and lemon juice. Add chives, carrots and beans, and then add broccoli and cauliflower, and finally savory and seasonings. Spoon into a casserole. Cover with breadcrumbs and grated cheese. Dot with butter. Bake at 180°C (350°F) for 30 minutes.

SCENTED GERANIUM (PELARGONIUM) PLATE 11

Family:	*Geraniaceae*
Species:	*Pelargonium fragrans, P. graveolens*
Plant:	perennial
Height:	15–120 cm
Soil:	average, dry, well-drained
Exposure:	sun
Propagation:	cuttings, sometimes seeds
Uses:	fragrance, decorative, culinary, medicinal

There is a huge variety of scented geraniums and a very interesting section of the fragrance garden can be made with them. They vary in height from a few centimetres, like the tiny-leafed nutmeg geranium, *Pelargonium fragrans*, up to the tall rose-scented *Pelargonium graveolens*.

A beautiful low hedge can be made of geraniums and the peppermint varieties – the velvet-leafed low-growing type and the skeleton leaf peppermint – can be grown in front of their taller cousins. Once you have smelt the glorious fragrance of the scented geraniums you will not rest until you have a variety in your own garden. Even the shape of their leaves is exquisite and they press beautifully.

The leaves have many uses, from pot-pourris to baking into cakes and custards, or even oiling furniture. Medicinally, they are beneficial for dysentery and diarrhoea. Use 5 leaves to 250 ml (1 cup) boiling water, steep, strain and take 1 tablespoon every half hour until the condition eases.

I have a favourite geranium pot-pourri recipe and an open bowl of this mixture at the bedside will aid sleeplessness; you can also fill pillows with it, or little sachets to put in your linen cupboard or amongst your lingerie.

GERANIUM POT-POURRI

Dry in the shade:
2 measures rose geranium
1 measure peppermint geranium
1 measure mixed nutmeg, lemon, orange and mint geraniums
½ measure crushed lemon peel
geranium oil

Mix the above ingredients, adding enough geranium oil to be pleasing. Stand covered for 10 days, shaking daily. Then use in bowls or pillows, reviving with a little geranium oil from time to time

Cuttings can be taken at any time of the year except in the coldest months. Choose a compact side shoot about 10 cm in length and pull off a small 'heel'. Remove lower leaves, dip into rooting hormone if you have it, and press into wet sand. (I first make

119

a small hole with a piece of stick, then firmly press the cutting down into the hole.) Keep protected and damp until rooted.

In colder areas, to ensure a good stock of new plants in spring take cuttings at the end of April. Choose a protected place to stand the boxes, make a frame over them and cover with plastic to make a miniature hot-house. Use stones to hold it down to ensure that no cold air creeps in but check watering daily as in the midday warmth the plants will sweat. Wait until spring is well underway before planting out as they are extremely frost tender.

Plant 90 cm apart as the rose-scented varieties grow to a good size very quickly. You can pick leaves as often as you like because with a good supply of compost they soon make new ones. Trim the bushes to keep them neat as the branches can become straggly.

In cold areas cover the plants with grass and pack handfuls of grass around the base. In the spring you can cut back frosted parts and with luck most of the plant will still be alive. Where the summers are hot and dry scented geraniums enjoy partial light/shade. Pinch growing tips back in the early stages of growth to encourage branching.

SOAPWORT

PLATE 26

Family: *Caryophyllaceae*
Species: *Saponaria officinalis*
Plant: perennial
Height: 15–60 cm
Soil: any
Exposure: sun, partial shade
Propagation: division, runners
Uses: medicinal

Soapwort is the pink perennial or Australian phlox, also known as Bouncing Bet, that invades everywhere in the garden and has amazing medicinal properties.

There is saponin present in the whole plant and it washes easily and well. It is excellent for restoring shining vitality to heat-damaged hair: boil up 6 handfuls of roots, stems, leaves and flowers in 2 litres (8 cups) of rainwater for 10 minutes. Remove the herb and add 6 more handfuls of the whole plant and boil up again in the same water for a further 10 minutes. Stand and allow to cool to a tepid heat, then strain. After shampooing, soak the hair for as long as possible in it. Rinse with fresh, warm water until all the soapiness has gone.

A weaker brew can be used for washing old tapestries and fabrics and a brew of 2 handfuls of herb to 1 litre (4 cups) boiling water is a soothing wash for eczema, grazes, skin rashes and wounds. It is a wonderful treatment for nappy rash too. Boil up fresh herb each time you use it.

Do not take internally as soapwort is poisonous to humans and animals and do not get it in the eyes as it burns slightly. If some should get into the eyes, rinse with tepid water several times.

Prepare a bed that has been lined with a 45 cm strip of heavy-duty plastic, add a few spadefuls of compost (2 spades to 1 square metre of soil), loosen well and plant root runners or pieces of root. Water well and thereafter give the bed a weekly watering. Apart from cutting off the dead flowers and adding an annual dressing of compost, soapwort needs little attention. The flowers, which seem to be prolific for most of the year except in mid-winter, are lovely in vases and in mixed bowls. One tends to curse its invasiveness but it is such a beneficial herb to grow if you make full use of its wonderful properties.

121

SORREL

PLATE 26

Family: *Polygonaceae*
Species: *Rumex acetosa*
Plant: perennial
Height: up to 60 cm
Soil: fairly rich, likes moisture
Exposure: sun, happy with afternoon shade
Propagation: seeds, division
Uses: culinary, medicinal

Fresh young sorrel leaves are delicious in salads and their acidic, piquant taste is most refreshing. Sorrel leaves cooked with spinach and cabbage can make a tasty dish, while sorrel soup is a gastronomic delight.

FRENCH SORREL SOUP

3 good handfuls sorrel leaves
4 tbls butter
50 ml (4 tbls) flour
25 ml (2 tbls) celery, chopped
25 ml (2 tbls) lovage, chopped
2 onions, chopped
1 litre (4 cups) chicken stock
250 ml (1 cup) cream
2 egg yolks, beaten
salt and pepper to taste

Chop sorrel leaves finely, after removing the thick midrib. Cook in the butter with the onions. Blend in flour and other ingredients, except egg yolks, leaving the stock till last. Stir well. Blend 125 ml (½ cup) of the hot soup with the egg yolks, beating well. Add to the rest of the soup. Heat thoroughly but slowly. Liquidise in a blender, then pour into bowls and serve sprinkled with chopped parsley. This soup is delicious hot or cold.

If you suffer from arthritis, gout, rheumatism or hyperacidity, do not eat sorrel. It is, however, beneficial for acne and skin ailments in the form of a poultice, and the root is tonic and diuretic.

If you plan to sow seed, sow as early in spring as you can for sorrel needs the summer's growing period to make a good sized bush. Plant out 45–60 cm apart. Always cut back flowering stems to keep the plant perennial.

Often well-established plants can be divided and the new young shoots successfully replanted. They do best in deeply dug, richly manured soil which is watered regularly.

SOUR FIG

Family: *Mesembryanthemaceae*
Species: *Carpobrotus edulis* (Hottentots' fig)
Plant: perennial
Height: low growing, spreading 3,5 metres
Soil: poor, sandy
Exposure: sun
Propagation: cuttings
Uses: medicinal

This South African indigenous ground cover is essential in the herb garden and requires no care except perhaps some restraint. It is a perfect cover for unsightly banks and slopes and needs very little water. Propagation is easy – just tuck a piece into the ground and keep wet for a few days and in no time at all it will send down roots and grow rapidly.

Chew a leaf tip if you have a sore throat and juice from the leaves is soothing for mouth infections, sore throats and indigestion. It is also an old indigenous remedy for diarrhoea and dysentery and the juice can be soothing and healing for burns. Sour fig grows easily on sand dunes near the coast and it is an antidote to bluebottle stings – rub the afflicted area with the juice from the leaves until soothed. It is also soothing for sunburn, heat rash, nettle stings and insect bites. A jam made from the ripened fruit is delicious and the fruit can also be dried and stored for making into gargles and mouth washes when the fresh plant is not at hand. Boil up 10 dried figs in 1 litre (4 cups) water.

Sour fig is not fussy about where it grows and seems to do well in any soil. I have grown it with success in black clay as well as on sand dunes at the coast and in both places it has grown richly and well, spreading vigorously.

There are several varieties of *Carpobrotus* but the medicinal properties of *C. edulis* seem to be the most effective.

Plant runners or pieces of stem 70–100 cm apart in well-dug soil. Clip back encroaching runners and plant them elsewhere. Sour fig grows fairly quickly once it has taken hold of its new position.

123

SOUTHERNWOOD (LAD'S LOVE)

PLATE 27

Family: *Compositae*
Species: *Artemisia abrotanum*
Plant: perennial
Height: 60 cm–1,2 m
Soil: dry, unfussy
Exposure: full sun
Propagation: division, cuttings
Uses: moth repellent, aromatic, fixative
Meaning: jest

With its pungent aroma, this woody-stemmed, green, feathery, decorative plant is a wonderful insect repellent. Sprays of southernwood placed between and behind rows of books will act as a fish-moth repellent.

Southernwood was once used as a 'strewing herb'; these were the aromatic plants which were spread on the dirt or wooden floors of homes in the fifteenth and sixteenth centuries to sweeten the air and keep the rooms insect free.

The leaves were added to a face cream which was believed to encourage the growth of a young man's beard – hence its other name, 'Lad's love'.

As it has antiseptic properties, it was also once used for all female ailments, and for ailments of a newborn baby, taken in the form of a brew of leaves sweetened with honey.

The group of artemesias is named after Artemis, or Diana, goddess of hunting or the woodlands, who was believed to watch over women and children and guard them at their time of birth.

I use southernwood as a low hedge around the herb garden as it can be very attractive when neatly clipped. Where its branches touch the ground it roots easily. A quick way to make rooted cuttings is to press a hoop of wire over a low-growing branch so that it touches the earth and let it send down roots. In a week or two the stem can be cut from the main plant, left briefly to harden and strengthen, and thereafter moved to its new site, a strong and healthy plant. Cuttings taken at any time of the year and pressed into wet sand root easily. Plant out 90 cm apart as the bushes grow as wide as they are tall.

Southernwood needs to be cut back at the end of the growing season – I usually find July is a good time as new buds form in early August and its spring growth is exuberant. All cut branches should be kept and dried as they are a most useful addition to insect-repellent sachets and help retain fragrance in pot-pourris. Southernwood is called 'garde-robe' in France and is used in sachets for keeping cupboards fresh and moth free. Keep the stripped branches for burning on winter fires and you will find that the fumes clear the air of cooking smells, while at a summer braaivleis they will keep mosquitoes away.

ST JOHN'S WORT

PLATE 15

Family:	*Guttiferae*
Species:	*Hypericum perforatum, H. revolutum,*
	H. aethiopicum
Plant:	perennial
Height:	15 cm–1,8 m
Soil:	not fussy
Exposure:	sun
Propagation:	cuttings
Uses:	medicinal

St John's wort was once a favoured garden shrub and could be found in gardens everywhere. There are over 500 varieties of *Hypericum*, seven of them native to South Africa. Recently *Hypericum perforatum*, widely used in European medicine, has appeared as a weed in the Cape Province. *Hypericum revolutum* and *Hypericum aethiopicum* are found in the Transvaal and all three have medicinal qualities. It is a wonderful healing herb, also known as 'Touch and Heal' and is one of nature's antibiotics. It is used for dysentery, sciatica, and as a wound dressing. It was also believed to possess magic charms to protect a home from harm and bunches of hypericum in the house are said to encourage fairies to visit!

Use the flowers in brews – 5 flowers to 250 ml (1 cup) boiling water – as a wash for wounds, rashes and burns. The same brew taken internally (37,5 ml or 3 tbls 3 times a day) is an effective treatment for worms, rheumatism, arthritis, hysteria and general nervousness.

Usually hypericum is undemanding and needs very little attention. The creeping varieties spread by runners and root easily and the other shrub-like varieties can be propagated by cuttings taken in spring and summer and pressed into wet sand. Try to pull off twigs with a heel attached and keep protected by making a plastic greenhouse tent over the box. Keep well watered until the cuttings have rooted, then transplant into bags and keep protected and damp until well established. Harden off by increasing the time in the sun each day and plant out 90 cm apart (30 cm if it is the low-growing type).

In August I have drastically trimmed back an ageing bush and it has burst forth with flowers and spring growth the following month.

125

STRAWBERRY

PLATE 27

Family: *Rosaceae*
Species: *Fragaria vesca*
Plant: perennial
Height: up to 15 cm
Soil: rich
Exposure: sun
Propagation: runners
Uses: culinary, medicinal
Meaning: esteem

The whole of the strawberry plant is refrigerant and soothing, rich in minerals and antiseptic. The fruit, a favourite in many lands, has strengthening, tonic and healing properties.

A tea can be made of the leaves, using 2 leaves to 250 ml (1 cup) boiling water. Steep and take half a cup morning and night to treat anaemia, thin blood, lowered vitality, lack of appetite, stomach and bowel disorders and liver ailments. The same brew is soothing for eczema, sore eyes and styes.

The fruit has many uses: it is a wonderful nerve tonic, cleans stains from the teeth and helps remove blemishes from the skin. Eat as much fruit as you can in strawberry season – which is a short one. The wild ground cover strawberry enjoys a longer season and its red fruits can often be found all the year round. Rubbed on the teeth they will whiten and brighten them.

A tea made from the fruit and leaves will aid irregular, painful menstruation. Take 4 sliced berries and 2 leaves per 250 ml (1 cup) boiling water and drink 125 ml (½ cup) 4 times a day until the condition is eased. The American Red Indians used strawberry leaves to prevent abortion and to bring down fevers.

Strawberry plants send out runners that can be clipped from the mother plant and replanted in a well-dug, well-manured bed, about 30 cm apart. Left undisturbed for two seasons, you will thereafter have an abundance of plants. These in turn will make new runners and the old mother stock can be discarded as the berries get smaller with the age of the plant. Plant the runners out into new beds in March, and in late September and October and you will have a wonderful crop. Dig in compost and old manure after the first crop and water weekly. An edging of strawberry plants in the herb garden will give you endless pleasure as they are neat and evergreen – and the bonus of their fruit is hard to beat.

TANSY

PLATE 28

Family: *Compositae*
Species: *Tanacetum vulgare, T. crispum*
Plant: perennial
Height: up to 90 cm
Soil: not fussy
Exposure: sun
Propagation: division, seeds
Uses: insecticide, medicinal
Meaning: I declare war against you

Tansy is a highly medicinal plant and one of the most mineral-rich of all herbs. It yields a brilliant yellow dye and was once used to colour cakes and confectionery. It is an excellent tonic – good for fevers, kidney ailments, digestive complaints, jaundice and menstrual disorders. It strengthens veins and is a remedy for high blood pressure and a weak heart. It is also an effective external application for varicose veins, soothing and reducing them, and is used for treating swellings, bruises, earache, styes and eye inflammations.

The standard lotion is 5 ml (1 tsp) chopped herb to 250 ml (1 cup) boiling water. The dose is 12,5 ml (1 tbls) of this brew to be taken three times daily before meals. Externally this same brew can be applied hot – soak a cotton cloth in the brew, wring it out and apply as hot as can be tolerated. Renew as it cools. *It is a very strong herb so take care not to exceed the standard dosage.*

To colour cakes use dried, powdered flowers, one dessertspoon added to 450 g (1 lb) flour.

Tansy grows easily and has a spreading habit. It dies back in winter and in spring can be thinned, replanting the rooted side shoots in new ground 60 cm apart. The aromatic leaves can be cut repeatedly and dried or chopped fresh to spread around ant holes as a deterrent. It is also a useful compost plant as it concentrates plenty of potassium in the soil.

Flower-heads dry well for winter arrangements – simply cut a bunch and hang upside down in a cool place to dry.

Tanacetum crispum is the curly tansy or sun fern that florists love. It, too, is an encroaching plant but it does not spread as vigorously as *T. vulgare*. Both grow easily from seed and if conditions are right, both seed themselves.

Owing to its strong pungent flavour and smell tansy combines with other herbs in homemade insecticide brews and is also very effective dried and sprinkled in insect-infected areas. Rubbed into a dog's coat, it will help keep fleas away.

TARRAGON

PLATE 28

Family: *Compositae*
Species: *Artemisia dracunculus, A. dracunculoides*
Plant: perennial
Height: up to 1 metre
Soil: light, well-drained, moderately rich
Exposure: sun, partial shade
Propagation: root cuttings, division
Uses: culinary

French tarragon, *Artemisia dracunculus*, has a thicker, coarser leaf and a stronger flavour than its close relative, Russian tarragon, or *Artemisia dracunculoides*. The French variety is not as vigorous nor as tough and does not propagate as easily.

No kitchen should be without tarragon and tarragon vinegar is an old favourite. Fill a bottle of good white vinegar with several sprays of tarragon. Place it in the sun for 100 hours (10 am to 4 pm daily) and during that period replace the tarragon sprays with fresh ones ten times. Then strain and rebottle and add a spray of fresh tarragon for decoration.

Do not cook tarragon, but rather add it chopped and raw to dishes just before serving. Finely chopped, it is delicious added to mayonnaise and seafood dressings and it makes an attractive decoration on all fish and chicken dishes. It does need to be used lavishly to get the full benefit of its flavour.

The plants die down in winter and send out new growth in spring. August is the time to separate the plants or to take cuttings and I have found that a piece of rooted cutting, pressed into loosely dug soil and kept moist, will quickly establish and give no further trouble. Separate the clump every second or third year and cut and re-plant invading runners 60 cm apart. All tarragon needs is a light, friable soil, with a weekly watering and a yearly dressing of compost, which should be dug in around the dormant plant in the winter, one spadeful per plant.

In autumn cut the plant back to 5 cm and cover with a layer of grass and leaves to protect the roots from winter frost. Tarragon tends to lose its flavour as it gets older, so do try always to have some new cuttings ready. One way of doing this is to dig up a clump, separate the side shoots from the mother plant, select the more robust suckers and replant them in the same place. Add a little compost and discard the mother plant. Water well until they establish themselves. Thereafter water once or twice a week – the plants tend to wilt on very hot days.

THYME

PLATE 28

Family:	*Labiatae*
Species:	*Thymus vulgaris, T. × citriodorus, T. serpyllum, T. aureus, T. argenteus*
Plant:	perennial
Height:	5–30 cm
Soil:	dry, light, good drainage
Exposure:	sun
Propagation:	cuttings, seeds
Uses:	culinary, medicinal
Meaning:	activity

There are several species of thyme, grown as ground covers, for flavouring and as ornamental plants.

Thymus vulgaris, the most commonly known thyme, is the favourite seasoning herb and grows in a woody-stemmed upright bush. It should be trimmed at frequent intervals as if it is not cut back pieces of it die off and the new growth is stunted. All the thymes make a pleasing border and *Thymus vulgaris* is a good edging plant for the culinary section of the herb garden.

Thymus vulgaris needs to be planted 30 cm apart and, as the roots go deep, the prepared bed for the plants needs to be dug deeply, with a light dressing of compost.

Thyme is one of the best loved herbs and historically has been associated with happiness, courage and general well-being. Thyme's medicinal uses are well known as antiseptic, digestive and anti-spasmodic cures. A brew of thyme, particularly the lemon-scented thyme, *T. × citriodorus*, is beneficial for coughs, colds and chills. Take 2 thumb-length pieces of thyme and pour over 250 ml (1 cup) boiling water. Stand for 5 minutes, strain and add a teaspoon or two of honey. Drink before going to sleep.

Thymus serpyllum, or creeping thyme, makes a beautiful ground cover and encourages fairies to come into your garden! It is easily propagated by cuttings and rooted pieces. It does need full sun (it becomes sparse and straggly in the shade) and makes a beautiful thyme walk border.

Thyme walks were a very popular garden design in the fifteenth, sixteenth and seventeenth centuries. The path would be just wide enough (a little over a metre) to accommodate the full skirts of the ladies. As they swept down the paths their skirts would brush the fragrant border of thyme and release into the air the antiseptic oils so important in those days of open sewers and their accompanying smells. A thyme walk often linked the gate to the front door of even the humblest cottage and bunches of thyme were used in the posies or tussie-mussies that were carried everywhere to combat stenches and odours.

Golden thyme, *Thymus aureus*, and silver thyme, *Thymus argenteus*, have wider leaf margins, a delicious lemon flavour and fragrance, and are good in rockeries as well as borders. Here again, cut them back when they begin to look straggly.

Layering is a good method of propagating *Thymus* varieties and often a hoop of

129

wire and a handful of soil to hold the branch in position is all that is needed to start a vigorous new plant. Cut from the mother plant and set out the new plants 30 cm apart in well-dug soil.

The lemon-flavoured thymes make delicious summer drinks and can also be added to pastries and cakes. *Thymus vulgaris* is used in meat, cheese, egg and fish dishes and is a delicious ingredient in the Bedouin Arab condiment *za'atar*.

THYME FRITTERS

20 ml (4 tsp) fresh thyme
50 ml (4 tbls, heaped) flour
190 ml (¾ cup) sour cream
juice of 1 lemon
salt and pepper
5 ml (1 tsp) baking powder
cooking oil

Mix all the ingredients. Have a pan with a little oil heating on the stove. Drop spoonfuls of batter into the oil, fry and turn to a golden brown. Drain on crumpled brown paper and serve immediately as an accompaniment to vegetable soup or as a snack.

1
2
3

1 Sour fig *p 123*
2 Southernwood *p 124*
3 Strawberry *p 126*

28

1 Valerian (garden) *p 55*
2 Tansy *p 127*
3 Tarragon *p 128*
4 Thyme *p 129*

1 Mullein (verbascum) *p 88*
2 Vinca rosea *p 131*
3 Violet *p 132*

1 Watercress *p 134*
2 Water lily *p 135*

VINCA ROSEA (PINK PERIWINKLE)

PLATE 29

Family:	*Apocynaceae*
Species:	*Vinca rosea (Star of Bethlehem)*
Plant:	perennial
Height:	up to 75 cm
Soil:	well-drained, sandy
Exposure:	sun
Propagation:	seeds
Uses:	medicinal

Vinca rosea is one of the easiest plants to grow and is a prolific spreader in the right conditions. It seems to survive drought, heat and wind and it grows quite happily both along the edges of the sand dunes at the sea as well as in harsh, dry conditions inland. Frost kills the top growth but in the spring it will shoot up from the root once again. There are pink and white forms and it is another of those old-fashioned plants so predominant in the gardens of long ago. It was then used for treating diabetes, chronic constipation and rheumatism and it is once again gradually coming back into favour.

Comprehensive research is now being conducted into the positive results of the dried ground root in the treatment of leukaemia and the plant is being cultivated for this reason in South Africa at present.

To use for rheumatism and arthritis make a tea using 3 leaves and 3 flowers to 250 ml (1 cup) boiling water. Stand for five minutes, then drain off the water and drink 125 ml (½ cup) morning and night.

The white juice can be used for warts and insect bites. For a wart apply the juice several times daily or squeeze on the fresh milky sap twice a day and cover with sticking plaster to exclude all air.

Vinca is a most rewarding plant to grow for once established in the garden it will seed itself endlessly and the young seedlings are easily transplanted. In August start off a few seeds in a moist, sand-filled tray. Keep protected until they reach the four-leaf stage, then harden off by placing in the sun for a lengthening period daily. Then plant out 30–45 cm apart in a bed that has been well dug over, with a spadeful or two of manure dug into it (2 spadefuls to a square metre). Water well and thereafter water weekly. They need no further care and their five-petalled, bright-eyed flowers are a constant pleasure throughout the summer. Seeds can be saved and planted in spring.

131

VIOLET

PLATE 29

Family:	*Violaceae*
Species:	*Viola odorata*
Plant:	perennial
Height:	about 15 cm
Soil:	moist, fairly rich
Exposure:	sun, prefers shade
Propagation:	division
Uses:	fragrance, medicinal
Meaning:	faithfulness

Violets have long been prized for their beauty, their fragrance and their medicinal qualities. The Africans use violet leaves as a cancer remedy and a leaf dipped into warm water is an excellent dressing for burns. Leaves are also drawing poultices and a syrup made with honey acts as a nerve tonic for children.

VIOLET NERVE TONIC

125 ml (½ cup) violet flowers
125 ml (½ cup) violet leaves
250 ml (1 cup) water
190 ml (¾ cup) honey

Place leaves and flowers into the water. Bring to the boil and add honey. Boil for 20 minutes over a low heat. Strain and bottle. Keep in the refrigerator. Dosage is 10 ml (2 tsp) 4–6 times a day for upset or highly strung children.

Violet flowers can be eaten to cure a headache; eat 5 to start with and 3 more an hour later. To clear coughs, whooping cough and thick mucousy throats, take 4–6 flowers in a cup of boiling water. Sweeten with honey and drink twice daily.

Violets grow easily and make an eye-catching border to paths and beds. They always look attractive and a tiny vase of violets can brighten up a room.

Use violet flowers in crystallising, and making ice-cream or jam. Violet vinegar dabbed onto the temples in the midsummer heat is wonderfully reviving and refreshing, particularly on long car journeys. Half fill a jar with fresh violets, cover with a good white vinegar, add a stick of cinnamon and stand in the sun for 10 days. Strain the vinegar and bottle into a screw-top bottle. Add a few violet flowers and a leaf or two tied together for decoration and identification.

As a constipation remedy, which is also suitable for children, violet syrup is most effective:

VIOLET SYRUP

25 ml (2 tbls) violet flowers
300 ml (½ pt) boiling water
12,5 ml (1 tbls) brown sugar

Pour boiling water over the flowers and stand for 5 hours. Strain, pressing juice through a sieve. Boil for 5 minutes with the sugar. Take 12,5 ml (1 tbls) on an empty stomach first thing in the morning, and then another mid-morning, and one mid-afternoon. Repeat whenever necessary.

I find in South Africa's heat, particularly in the Transvaal, violets prefer to grow in shade or partial shade. I have grown them in full sun, too, and, although not so lush or dark green, they have done well. Prepare a bed of well dug in compost and a little old manure – about 2 spadefuls to 1 square metre – and water well. Divide up violet clumps, spacing them about 30 cm apart. I keep them shaded for the first few days by sticking a few leafy twigs into the ground around them. Be sure to keep them damp and you shouldn't have any losses.

WATERCRESS

PLATE 30

Family: *Cruciferae*
Species: *Nasturtium officinale*
Plant: annual, biennial
Height: 15 cm
Soil: damp, swampy
Exposure: partial shade
Propagation: seeds, rooted stems
Uses: medicinal, culinary

Watercress is easy to grow from seed as long as the soil is never allowed to dry out. It seeds itself readily along furrows and in swampy ground. Ideally it should be grown along the edges of furrows in running water but not everyone is lucky enough to have a stream at the bottom of the garden, especially with the drought South Africa experiences from time to time. I have been successful in growing a clump or two under a dripping tap and in a pot it does well for a season. Stand the pot in a bowl of water and keep swilling out and topping up with fresh water. If the water becomes stagnant the plants will die off and if the ground is swampy they need to be hosed down every few days.

In commercial watercress production the herb is grown in shallow tanks with a base of soil and water, just enough to float the crowns, and the water is kept moving slowly and topped with fresh water daily.

Watercress is high in vitamin C and is used as an anti-scurvy treatment. It is a tonic herb and is an effective treatment for anaemia, rickets and weak eyesight. Combined with honey it is a good old-fashioned cough remedy. Even the juice applied to a blemish or pimple will quickly heal it.

A variety known as garden cress, *Lepidium sativum*, grows well in a cool, damp place in the garden and it, too, has the same medicinal properties. Treat it as an annual and all through the year grow it on a cotton wool-lined tray with mustard seed. Keep moist and watch the seeds sprout and grow quickly. Cut off with kitchen scissors when thumb length in height and use as a filling for sandwiches or sprinkle over roast chicken or steaks.

Watercress is really a cool weather crop so in the warmer areas of the country you would do best to sow it in autumn for a winter salad crop.

Sprinkle seeds onto a moist patch of ground. Cover with a little sand and a fine sprinkling of compost. Shade with hessian and never allow the bed to dry out. Once the seeds are at the four-leaf stage remove the hessian and keep the seedlings moist. Pick the outer lower leaves for salads, or the side-shoot rosettes of leaves.

WHITE WATER LILY

PLATE 30

Family: *Nymphaeaceae*
Species: *Nymphaea alba*
Plant: perennial
Height: from submerged roots to flowers: up to 1 metre,
                     depending on depth of water
Exposure: sun, partial shade
Propagation: root stock division
Uses: medicinal
Meaning: purity of heart

The water lily gets its name from the Greek *nymphae* or 'water nymph', and the beautiful ethereal flowers of the white pond lily, *Nymphaea alba*, are always a great source of pleasure to all who see them. While it is often cultivated as an ornamental aquatic herb, few people are aware of its numerous medicinal uses.

The root is the medicinal part. Take a piece 18 cm long and shave it into fine pieces. Place in a pot, add 300 ml (½ pt) cold water and heat gently for 5 minutes, keeping below boiling point. Steep for 3–4 hours, strain and use this brew for bowel ailments, taking 12,5 ml (1 tbls) morning and night (more often if necessary, up to ten times during the day). It is a gentle soothing treatment for children with diarrhoea – give a dessert-spoon of the brew six times during the day. Externally the same brew can be used as a gargle for throat ailments, as a wash for mouth ulcers and as a nasal douche for congestion of nasal passages and sinusitis. It also makes a soothing vaginal douche, is effective in kidney ailments and reduces internal inflammations. The leaves, washed and warmed, can be applied externally to treat skin rashes, sores, sores of the genital organs and wounds. They make a soothing dressing for sunburn too.

If you should be lucky enough to have a pond in your herb garden, the water lily is an easy plant to grow. Fill a large clay pot with rich compost and soil, press the root rhizome of the lily well into it and secure the pot between stones in the pond. I have used a moss-lined wire basket and planted the root rhizome well into it but it does break up in time and become unsteady so a large old-fashioned clay pot would be better in the long run. New plants can be divided from the main rhizome every second spring and planted in separate water lily pots. The water lily can also be grown quite successfully in a large tub as long as it is topped up with fresh water from time to time. It needs its feet in good compost and every two years will benefit from being repotted with fresh compost.

WILD PINEAPPLE

PLATE 11

Family:	*Liliaceae*
Species:	*Eucomis undulata* (*E. autumnalis*)
Plant:	perennial bulb, dies down in winter
Height:	up to 1 metre
Soil:	average
Exposure:	sun, partial shade
Propagation:	seed
Uses:	medicinal

Eucomis comes from the Greek *eukomes* which means 'beautiful hair' or 'top knot' and refers to the tuft of leaves at the top of the long flowering spike. The eucomis is valued as an anti-witchcraft plant and is nowadays seldom found growing in the wild as witchdoctors use a decoction of the leaves for washing in as a protection against being bewitched. A *kxapumpu* growing in your garden is therefore a valuable protection herb. The 10 cm bulb can be used to relieve abdominal pain and distention – 5 ml (1 tsp) of bulb shaved into 250 ml (1 cup) boiling water. Drink 2 tablespoons every half hour until the pain is soothed. Local Africans use a brew of the chopped and shaved bulb and leaves as a cure for excess conviviality.

Eucomis is unfussy as to soil type but benefits from a good weekly watering. It can grow up to 1 metre tall and spread as wide, so plant bulbs 60–90 cm apart in well-dug and composted soil. Ripe seeds from the flowering head can be placed in individual pots or bags to establish a good sized bulb before planting out into the garden. Do not overwater the new bulbs or they will rot but also take care not to allow them to dry out too much.

The whole plant dies down in the winter. In spring clear away the frosted, dried leaves, dig in a little compost mulch with leaves and water well once a week.

WILDE ALS

PLATE 31

Family:	*Compositae*
Species:	*Artemisia affra*
Plant:	perennial
Height:	up to 180 cm
Soil:	poor
Exposure:	sun
Propagation:	seeds, cuttings
Uses:	medicinal

Wilde als is used medicinally by black and white South Africans with such wonderful results that it deserves pride of place in the herb garden.

It is used as a treatment for colic, respiratory ailments, stomach disorders, coughs, colds, sore throats, eye infections, earache, croup and whooping cough. A wilde als tea is a tried and tested flu remedy and preventive, while a few leaves rubbed onto travel weary feet will soothe away aches and pains. A standard brew is a sprig the length of a thumb in 250 ml (1 cup) boiling water. Sweeten with honey and drink a little several times a day. Give a teaspoon or two to a child with colic every few minutes to relieve the discomfort.

Wilde als sets seed easily and seeds readily. I have also had success with cuttings. Choose a long, sturdy branch and cut it into 12 cm lengths. Press into a box of wet sand, trim off a few leaves at the base of each piece, keep shaded and moist and plant out when sturdy and well rooted. Harden off by placing in the sun for some time, starting gradually, then plant out 180 cm apart into well-dug soil.

Trim back in spring for the tips may be frosted in winter and keep tidy by cutting back from time to time.

Save all the trimmed pieces and dry by hanging in bunches in a cool, airy shed. Use in moth repellent sachets or sprinkle near ants' nests. Branches can be placed under boxes in store-rooms and in amongst books to repel moths and fish-moths.

Do not over-water wilde als as this indigenous plant is used to growing on mountain slopes with erratic rainfall.

WORMWOOD

PLATE 31

Family:	*Compositae*
Species:	*Artemisia absinthium*
Plant:	perennial
Height:	30–120 cm
Soil:	any, not fussy
Exposure:	sun
Propagation:	cuttings, division
Uses:	medicinal, insecticide, culinary
Meaning:	absence

Wormwood is an amazing drought-resistant herb. It grows in any soil and needs no attention other than an occasional watering and cutting back of straggly, spent growth.

The whole plant is pungent and bitter tasting, owing to the presence of 'absinth', the bitter principle which is used to make the famous green liqueur. The over-use or misuse of absinth was believed to cause epilepsy but it is a wonderful healing herb nonetheless. In antiquity wormwood was chosen as the symbol of health and healers had the leaf painted on their doors as a sign to their patients. That great healer John the Baptist wore a woven girdle of wormwood, hence its other name, 'St John's Girdle'.

Wormwood is primarily antiseptic, vermifuge and narcotic. It is used in treating fevers, worms, constipation and jaundice. It will restore a flagging appetite, aid digestion and cure diarrhoea and dysentery. It is a famous 'women's' herb, used for giving relief in morning sickness, preventing a threatened miscarriage and treating obesity. It is also a wonderfully soothing aid for earache and ear infections. It is an insect repellent if rubbed on the skin or bruised and kept in a bowl nearby. The brew is made by adding three 15 cm long sprigs to 600 ml (1 pt) boiling water. Sweeten with honey to disguise the bitterness of the herb and take 10 ml morning and night for a maximum of four days. *As it is a potent herb do not exceed the dosage.* If it is exceeded or if it is taken for over-long periods and in too strong a brew, it will dilate the blood vessels and have an increased action on the heart. In fact, as a general rule if there is ever any doubt about a herb, consult a homoeopathic doctor or a knowledgeable herbalist before using it.

With the proper dosage, taken with care, this highly esteemed herb will safeguard and strengthen the body, particularly the female body.

Dried, powdered wormwood is an insecticide in itself and can be sprinkled around ants' nests and fruit trees to deter ants and fruit flies. Use it in a brew to spray for aphids and mites. I take half a bucket of wormwood branches, well pressed down, and then fill the bucket with boiling water, add a cupful of washing powder and allow to draw. Strain and use as a spray. A bath of wormwood will chase fleas off a dog and dried wormwood is also helpful in keeping weevils out of stored grain.

Propagation is quick, easy and always successful – merely divide the plants and replant branches into well-dug soil that has had a little compost and old manure added to it (a spadeful of each to a square metre). Water well and keep moist for the first few days. Cuttings can be handled in the same way – trim off excess leaves and stem, press into a prepared bed and keep moist until established. Thereafter water weekly or occasionally. Plant 1 metre apart as it becomes a rather large bush. Clip back to neaten at the end of summer and save the leaves for use in sachets and insect-repelling pot-pourris.

YARROW

PLATE 31

Family: *Compositae*
Species: *Achillea millefolium, A. filipendulina, A. ageratifolia*
Plant: perennial
Height: 30–60 cm
Soil: any
Exposure: sun
Propagation: division, runners
Uses: medicinal

Yarrow is an old-fashioned garden flower that has been used for hundreds of years as a wound healer. Achilles used to heal his wounds and those of his soldiers by using a yarrow dressing, hence the name *Achillea*.

Yarrow is a most attractive plant throughout the year and it really deserves a prominent place in the garden. In spring and summer its flowers are a mass of pink and white and after their long period of bloom, the stems can be cut down into the ferny leaves.

It has so many medicinal uses that it is one of the most valued herbs. Not only does it heal wounds, it stops bleeding and reduces fevers and can be used as a quinine substitute in the treatment of malaria. It is used in the treatment of hypertension and coronary thrombosis and because of its astringent properties it is used in cases of excessive menstruation, diarrhoea and dysentery. It is also soothing and effective in treating pneumonia, rheumatism and sore throats. It is a diuretic and skin cleanser and can be used to make a lotion which is a soothing application for haemorrhoids. Surely few plants have such an amazing range of treatments? The standard brew is a handful of leaves to 1 litre boiling water. Allow to steep for 10 minutes, then strain and drink a wineglassful 3 times daily.

There are several varieties of yarrow. The coarser leafed, yellow-flowered *Achillea filipendulina* ('Cloth of Gold') and the Greek yarrow, *Achillea ageratifolia*, are wonderful for flower arrangements, especially dried, but neither has the medicinal properties of the common yarrow, *Achillea millefolium*.

Yarrow is a plant doctor, too. Planted near an ailing plant it will revive it, restoring it to health, and it keeps all its neighbouring plants free of insects. Leaves and flowers dry well and can be added to pot-pourris.

Propagation is quick and easy – just dig the side runners out and plant in a new position. Every 3 or 4 years separate and divide the clump and dig in some compost and old manure. Plant out at a distance of 30 cm and water well. Yarrow is unfussy as to its soil requirements and it is a lovely cut flower.

3
HARVESTING AND DRYING
OF HERBS

The care which you have exercised in planting your herbs can easily be to no avail through incorrect harvesting and drying.

Seeds can be collected at the end of the season's growth and should be sorted and stored in clearly marked envelopes or packets when they are quite dry. If roots are to be harvested the plant must reach its full maturity at the end of summer before it is dug up.

To harvest the leaves from a plant the general rule is to pick the leaves once the plant starts flowering. This is the time when the active principles of the plant are of the best quality and it is then that the oils which give the herb its distinctive aroma and fragrance are the most concentrated.

Choose a sunny, warm morning to do your picking, after the night's dew has dried from the leaves and before the sun gets too hot. The best picking time in South Africa's summer heat is from 8 am to 10 am. Some annuals flower early in the season and if you cut them back they will grow enough for a second harvest in autumn. *Basil, dill, fennel* and *celery* are amongst those which often give a second picking but do not cut back too vigorously the first time. After the summer the whole plant can be cut back and dried.

Shrubby perennials such as *thyme, lemon balm, marjoram, lavender* and *rosemary* can be cut back to encourage bushy, compact growth and of course each twig can be saved and dried.

Some annual herbs, among them *anise, caraway, coriander, dill* and *celery*, produce tasty seeds that are used in cookery and flavouring. Harvest these as soon as they start to turn brown but before they fully ripen and scatter far and wide. Cut the entire seed head off into a brown paper bag. Label and date it and store until completely dry, then clean and sort the seeds and store in screw-top glass bottles or well-corked pottery jars.

For drying herbs you will need a few screens which you can easily make yourself: take a frame made from wood or metal and stretch a shade cloth or loosely woven piece of hessian over it. The green herbs can be put directly onto the screen and dried in the shade in an airy shed or garage. For small quantities of herbs, a spread-open newspaper will suffice, but be sure to turn the herbs daily and never pack too many on top of each other. *Rose petals* dry well if thinly spread on newspaper. Always dry the herbs in the shade and in our summer heat this will only take a few days. Once they are dry and brittle to the touch, separate the sticks and leaf stalks and rub down the bigger leaves to storable sizes. Have ready labelled bottles or packets and always work with only one kind of plant, completing its storage before starting the next, or the flavours will intermingle and your effort will be wasted.

Choose airtight storage containers so that moist air cannot be re-absorbed. In the humidity of the coastal regions, herbs can be dried in a cool oven overnight at the lowest heat possible. Try drying the herbs first a few days before placing in the oven to dry off some of the initial moisture.

The dried material is only one-eighth the weight of the harvested herb and I find that after about four months the flavour and goodness of the dried plant have usually deteriorated, so it is best to use up the dried material quickly.

For pot-pourris and pomanders the summer flowers can be dried in the same way to keep their colours brilliant (be sure no sun touches them) and if you want whole flowers in your pot-pourris bunches can be hung upside down from the roof to dry.

The moisture content of most plants is 70% and the aim is to dry the material as quickly as possible to maintain the aroma and flavouring to some degree. A drying period of 3 to 5 days is ideal.

Mixed Herbs

A useful mixed herb recipe for savoury dishes – soups, stews and pies – is the combination of equal quantities of *thyme*, *marjoram*, chopped *celery* and chopped *sage*. To this can be added a *bay* leaf or two and some *parsley* or chopped *chives* and a little *garlic* to vary the flavours. When a recipe calls for 'a pinch of herbs' this is the basic mixture, but of course you can vary it to your own taste.

Bouquet Garni

Ingredients vary in several recipe books but through the years I have found the following recipe to be the most delicious, without being too obtrusive. Again, you can vary it to suit your own taste.

Use 15 cm squares of butter muslin to tie up the herbs. If you use your own freshly dried herbs you can use the bouquet garni bag two or three times over again; simply rinse it under running water after it has been removed from the soup or stew and hang it up to dry. It may look unappealing but the flavour is still there!

Basic combination:

1 bay leaf per bag
Equal quantities of:
    thyme
    marjoram or oreganum
    sage
    parsley
    rosemary
    lovage or celery

Mix and place in small heaps in each bag – usually about 2 heaped teaspoons per bag, plus the bay leaf – and tie up securely.

POT-POURRIS

In the making of pot-pourris, the three most important things to remember are the fixative, the spices and the combination of predominant fragrances. Recipes and uses are legion but here are some basic rules for successful pot-pourris.

Dry Pot-Pourri
Basic ingredients are: *rose petals, lavender*, scented leaves such as *scented geraniums* or *lemon verbena*, other fragrant flowers like *honeysuckle, jasmine* and *violets*.

Fixatives
Ground *lemon* and *orange peel*, powdered *orris root* (any old-fashioned irises can be dug up, washed, trimmed of fibrous roots and minced – then dried, crushed and pounded if not minced finely enough), crushed *vanilla pods, sandalwood* raspings and minced *vetiver root*.

Quantity: use 12,5 ml (1 tbls) to 750 ml (3 cups) leaves and flowers (approximately). Use very little vanilla as it is very strong.

Spices
The usual mixture is equal quantities of *cinnamon, cloves* and *nutmeg*, all finely ground. *Coriander, allspice* and *cardamom* can also be added to give an unusual fragrance, and here use 12,5 ml (1 tbls) per 4 cups of flowers and leaves.

Top Notes
Essential flower oils are expensive but necessary and several are available. Choose the predominant flower in your recipe – for example lavender or rose – and use that oil as your top note. Your own taste will dictate how much you use but a general rule is 5 ml (1 tsp) oil to 6 cups leaves and flowers. Add the oils to the mixture last of all and keep well sealed. Shake daily for a month, then fill sachets, bags, pillows or containers with the wealth of the summer garden.

Additions
Many other items can be added to pot-pourris to give colour, texture and fragrance, such as the various *mints, rosemary, santolina*, tiny dried *kumquats* and underdeveloped *oranges, naartjies* and *lemons*. *Orange* and *lemon* leaves and a small quantity of insecticide plants such as *khakibos, wilde als, southernwood, wormwood* or *pyrethrum* can be added to make the pot-pourri insect repellent.

Whole flowers of *larkspur, statice* and *strawflowers*, dried whole *rosebuds, petria* and *cornflowers* can be added to give colour if your pot-pourri is to be decorative, contained in glass jars, as these flowers will keep their brightness.

Moist Pot-Pourri
Take a large crock with a well-fitting lid. For the bottom layer use partially dry *rose petals* (dried to a leather-like consistency) and immediately over this sprinkle a layer of sea salt, not the iodised sort. Then add a layer of fresh *jasmine* flowers followed by another layer of salt, a layer of fresh *lemon verbena* leaves, salt and a layer of *violets*, salt and a layer of *honeysuckle* flowers. Continue to add layers of salt and flowers for a few days – it does not all have to be done on one day – and all the while keep the jar covered but not tightly closed. If the flowers are large, eg gardenias or heliotrope sprays, allow them to dry partially before putting them into the jar. The smaller flowers, such as jasmine, honeysuckle and lavender, can go into the jar freshly picked.

Continue to add alternate layers until the jar is filled. Place a light covering over the jar and leave to stand for 10 days or up to 2 weeks in a dark place. Then empty the mixture into a large basin and break it up. Add crushed *cinnamon*, *nutmeg* and *cloves* – a half cup to every 6 cups of mixture. Add crushed dried *orange* and *lemon peel* and a few drops of essential oil, one cup of this mixture to every 6 cups of mixture. Blend well and return to the crock and leave tightly covered for 6 weeks. Shake frequently to keep the ingredients well mixed. Then again turn out the now matured mixture into a basin, add a few more drops of essential oil – whatever your predominant flower fragrance is – to your own taste and another half cup of crushed *cloves*, *nutmeg* and *coriander*. Seal again for a month, shaking daily, and then fill pottery jars and dark glass bottles with the pot-pourri. Revive with essential oil and a little brandy to keep it moist.

The moist pot-pourri should not be left to stand open as it dries out the fragrance. Keep it in sealed containers which may be opened from time to time to allow the fragrance out; add a few drops of essential oil now and again.

It was this mixture that gave pot-pourri its name – 'rotten pot'! It is unattractive to look at as the petals lose their colours and darken and the fragrant leaves turn almost black, but it is an everlasting pot-pourri. I have some which was made seventeen years ago and it is still as gloriously fragrant today as it was the day I made it.

POMANDERS

Traditionally pomanders were small pieces of a strongly scented fixative called ambergris which comes from the intestine of the sperm whale. The French term 'pomme d'ambre' or 'apple of ambergris' is the origin of the word pomander and these tiny apple-shaped pieces of ambergris were enclosed in little cases of silver, gold, wood or ivory and worn around the neck on a chain as a protection against infection and unpleasant smells. Modern pomanders, filled with a pot-pourri mixture, are made of china, porcelain or clay and they have holes in them to allow the scent to pass through.

A citrus pomander is a deliciously different idea and very easy to make. Take an orange and, using a knitting needle, make small holes, close together, in the skin. Press cloves into the holes so that they push easily into the fruit. Over the clove-studded fruit sprinkle a tablespoon or two of powdered orris root and then place the orange in a brown paper packet. Keep scooping and sprinkling orris root over the fruit in the packet for a month, turning it daily. I press a hairpin into the fruit to make a loop through which to thread a ribbon and hang the pomander in a cupboard to keep it smelling fragrantly fresh.

FREEZING HERBS

Some of the more tender herbs such as *tarragon*, *borage*, *salad burnet*, *sweet basil*, *dill*, *parsley*, *comfrey* and *chives* can be frozen satisfactorily and, as these herbs do not really dry well, freezing is a solution if you do not have access to fresh herbs all the year round.

Tie the herbs in bundles with string and blanch in unsalted boiling water for about 5 seconds, holding onto the string so that you can lift them out easily. Cool them quickly by dipping into a bowl of iced water, then fold into foil or freezer bags, labelling each carefully. If you chop the leaves before packaging they will be ready for use as soon as they are removed from the freezer. A good idea is to put separate recipe amounts in each small bag so that small quantities are available as you need them. They can be placed still frozen directly into the food or sauce you are cooking but if they are to go into salads defrost them beforehand.

HERB TEAS

Herb teas are perhaps the most popular preparations in the using of herbs and they are simple to make, with either fresh or dried herbs. They were once the favoured drinks in nearly all households.

Generally, the most satisfactory quantity is, per 250 ml (1 cup) boiling water, a twig of herb the length of your thumb. A sachet of rooibos tea is an acceptable addition as it does not make you feel that you are drinking only pale green hot water!

For a pot of tea for four, for example, use 2 sprigs of *rosemary, lemon balm, mint* (only one sprig of peppermint as it is very strong), *bergamot, lemon verbena, chamomile, winter savory* or *lavender,* and one sachet of rooibos. Pour in boiling water as you would in making ordinary tea, allow to steep for a few minutes, then pour. Sweeten with honey if you have a sweet tooth, but never use milk or artificial sweeteners.

If using dried herbs, use one heaped teaspoon per cup.

The flavours of the teas will become your personal choice and to describe their flavours in a few words is impossible. It is exciting to experiment yourself to find the ones you like most, but all are good, healthy and enjoyable.

HERB VINEGARS

Many herbs can be preserved in vinegar and herb flavoured vinegars enhance salads and savoury dishes, giving the healthful benefit of the herbs at the same time.

As a general guide, pack into a bottle herbs that will impart flavour, such as *thyme, basil, garlic, rosemary, dill, celery, chives, elder* flowers, *mint, marjoram, oreganum* or *sage.* Fill the bottle with vinegar and place it in the sun for 100 hours – counting the hours from 10 am to 4 pm, as the early morning sun and the late afternoon sun are not strong enough to make a difference. During that time remove and replace the herbs with fresh herbs 10 times (or less, depending on how strong you want the vinegar).

Then strain through butter muslin into a clean bottle and push a fresh sprig of the herb into it as decoration and identification. Cork well and use in all recipes that call for vinegar.

HERB OILS

Herbs combine beautifully with oils. These can be used in cooking, while some special herbs are perfect for the bath.

In general, press sprigs of fragrant herbs into a jar, cover with oil, stand in the sun for 2 weeks, then use. Do not strain and change the herbs for fresh ones; the oil is very easily able to absorb the fragrance and flavour of the herb.

Savoury Oil

For salad dressings choose olive oil or sunflower seed oil. Pour 2 cups of oil into a bottle or jar. Boil and add:

2 sprigs rosemary
6 sprigs thyme
3 hot red chillis
6 black peppercorns
1 large clove garlic that has been peeled and halved

Seal tightly and stand in the sun for 2 weeks, shaking daily. Use for salads or marinades.

Bath Oil
For a fragrant, skin-softening bath oil, into 2 cups of unperfumed soluble bath oil (available at chemists) add the following:

2 sprigs rosemary
2 sprigs lemon thyme
1 sprig lemon verbena
10 lavender flowers
10 drops lavender oil

Seal, shake well and leave in the sun for 2 weeks, shaking daily. Use a little in your bath and enjoy the pampering and soothing treatment to your skin.

Oil for Winter
A good oil for winter is:

2 cups unperfumed soluble bath oil
rind of 1 lemon, thinly pared
4 lemon leaves
10 cloves
2 sprigs rosemary
2 sprigs bergamot
10 drops jasmine oil

Seal, shake well and leave in the sun for 2 weeks. Use sparingly each night in your bath during the winter. A little of this oil rubbed into rough elbows and heels is soothing and smoothing.

Any herbs that appeal to you can be used in this way. I find the nicest are: *elder* flowers, *lavender, sage, rosemary, lemon thyme, mints, yarrow* flowers and leaves, *bergamot*, and the *scented geraniums*.

1 Wilde als *p 137*
2 Wormwood *p 138*
3 Yarrow *p 140*

1 Celery *p 35*
2 Chervil *p 37*
3 Dill *p 49*
4 Fennel *p 52*
5 Lovage *p 78*
6 Parsley *p 98*

4
PROPAGATION OF PLANTS
IN GENERAL

There are four main ways of propagating herbs – seeds, root division, layering and taking cuttings. In Chapter 2 the individual herbs have in their descriptions the most appropriate means of propagation but as an easy reference the framework set out below may be useful.

Seed sowing in containers
There are a number of advantages in starting seeds in containers in sheltered positions. Perennial herbs which often take a long time to germinate can be started indoors late in winter and can be moved outside to harden off when the spring comes. Indoors one can control the temperature and soil conditions and can therefore produce superior seedlings, and germination is far more satisfactory.

Commercially made seed boxes are probably the easiest to handle and they already have drainage holes. Any container can be adapted, however – strong cartons and tomato boxes can be lined with plastic and, with a few drainage holes, these can be quite satisfactory. Place a few small stones at the bottom of the container and then fill with your soil mixture to within 15 mm of the top. The soil mixture needs to be loose, well draining and yet one which will hold water. I find equal parts sand, garden loam and a fine, well-matured compost is a good basic mixture. Sieve through a 6 mm mesh screen to remove any clods and sticks and firm down well in the container.

Sprinkle the seeds evenly over the surface and cover with a depth of soil approximately twice the diameter of the seed. Water carefully, using a fine spray so as not to wash the seeds out of the soil or expose them. Another way of watering is to soak the bottom of the seed tray in a pan of water so that the moisture is drawn up into the soil by capillary action. The secret of successful seed sowing is to ensure that the soil never dries out in those first critical weeks of germination.

Label the containers clearly so that you are sure which seeds you have sown and cover them with a pane of glass or hessian to protect them from the drying effect of the wind. The seeds do not need light until they have sprouted but they do need fresh air to prevent fungus formation so lift off the cover for an hour or two each day, always checking to see that the soil has not dried out.

After germination the container can be moved to partial shade where there is good light but not full sun. Turn the container daily so that the seeds can receive equal exposure to light. Always keep moist but be sure not to over-water as at this stage the seedlings are liable to damp off. When two sets of true leaves have formed the seedlings can be transplanted into bigger containers or, if sturdy enough, can be planted into prepared beds in the garden and shaded until stronger.

If you want the plants to establish well, plant into the new containers in a richer mixture of soil – 2 parts garden loam, 1 part river sand and 1 part sifted peat moss or compost. Space the seedlings wider apart, at least 5 cm, and water carefully until well established.

Once the plants are strong and big enough, place the seed box in the sun for increasing periods during the few days before planting out in order to strengthen them. Plant out in a prepared bed which should be well dug with compost and have a good amount of leaf mould added to it. As a general guide use 2 spadefuls of compost and 1 spadeful of leaf mould or old manure to 1 square metre of soil.

Planting seeds directly into the garden
Any seeds can be sown into the garden as soon as all danger of frost has passed and the soil has begun to warm up.

Some seeds that do well sown directly into their site are *mealie, calabash, morning glory, nasturtium, sunflower, globe artichoke, castor oil, cornflower, marigold, mustard, radish, angelica, cress, sweetpea, pumpkin* and *squash*.

First choose a place that is suitable for the plant and then turn the soil to a depth of about 30 cm, breaking up the clods. If the soil drains poorly add organic compost, leaf mould, chopped hay or peat moss to lighten it. Fork and level well, then make shallow drills (draw the rake over the soil to indicate the lines) and sow the seeds into these drills, spacing them well. Cover with soil to the depth of about twice the diameter of the seed, firm down well with the back of the rake and water with a fine spray, taking care not to expose the seeds. Label the row so that you are sure of what you have planted as new seedlings all look very similar.

In South Africa's heat and wind it is usually necessary to make a low protective frame of sticks. I use forked sticks driven into the soil at each of the four corners of the bed. Onto these I tie long sticks or reeds to form the frame, as well as a few cross reeds tied at intervals. Arrange a hessian covering over the frame, securing it in place with string. Alternatively a thin layer of thatching grass over the frame will do as well. Secure it by tying sticks over it to weight it down against the wind. I find about 20 cm above the soil is all that is needed for the height of the frame; anything higher will need side flaps to counteract the slanting rays of the hot spring sunshine. Where it is difficult to cover the plants with a shade area I make a small dam around each seed, or a long row of built up earth, and put dried leaves and grass into it to create a little shade for those newly germinating seeds. Do remember to water at least twice a day to ensure that the seeds remain moist.

The germination period for most annual seeds is 12–14 days and a little longer for perennials – sometimes from 3 weeks up to one month. Throughout this period the soil must be kept moist.

Broadcasting is another seed planting method. This is when you want to cover a certain area instead of planting in rows. Prepare the soil as above, water well and scatter the seeds evenly over the area. Cover with sand and water and shade the area as you would rows of seeds.

Propagating by cuttings
Rooting cuttings or slips is perhaps the easiest method of propagating and so much faster than sowing seeds. Many herbs grow well from cuttings, for example *lavender, rosemary, sage*, the *thymes, marjoram, oreganum, pineapple sage, lemon balm, ber-*

148

gamot, *southernwood*, *lemon verbena*, *bay*, *catnip*, *feverfew*, *horehound*, *hydrangea*, *hyssop*, *hypericum*, *ivy*, *mint*, *pig's ear*, *rock-rose*, *rue*, *santolina*, *sour fig*, *tansy*, *wilde als* and *wormwood*.

Cuttings can be taken at any time during the growing season from healthy, well-established plants. Strong new tip growth makes the best cuttings. Make the cutting just below a leaf bud or node, using a sharp knife or clippers. The length of the cutting should be between 8–15 cm. Keep the cuttings damp by placing them between layers of wet newspaper or cloth and keep them out of the sun until you are ready to plant them. Have seed boxes ready, about 10 cm in depth and filled with river sand. If you have just a few cuttings, a pot or a jam tin will suffice as long as it has good drainage (a few stones in the bottom of the container will help).

Wet the sand thoroughly and make a row of holes with a stick, about 5–8 cm in depth. Strip the lower leaves from the cuttings and press each one into its prepared hole. You can first dip the cut end into a hormone rooting powder if you like. Press down firmly and complete the rows. Water again and place in a protected, warm place in the shade. If the cuttings are taken before winter, make a miniature greenhouse over them by covering them with plastic, supported on a frame or wire arches, the edges tucked under stones to keep out draughts.

It usually takes from a month to 7 weeks for the cuttings to take and to form strong roots of their own and in all this time they must not be allowed to dry out. Give them a little time in the sun to harden off before transplanting and when you remove them from their seed tray be careful how you take them out – shake the box out gently on its side so as not to pull away the tender new roots.

Transplant into prepared beds which have compost and manure (2 spades compost, 1 manure to 1 square metre) well dug into the area. Make a hole, place the cutting into it, cover the roots with soil, press down firmly and water well. Do not let the cuttings dry out and mulch with coarse compost. Once the plants are established water regularly once or twice weekly.

Layering

Creeping herbs such as the *mints*, the *thymes*, *catmint*, *winter savory*, *ivy*, *southernwood*, *honeysuckle*, the *jasmines*, *elder* and *germander*, when brought into contact with the soil, will take root while they are still attached to the parent plant. Many herbs in any case send down roots naturally from branches that touch the ground, so this is a very quick and easy way to make new plants.

Select a strong, healthy branch growing close to the ground. Dig a shallow hole below it and fill with sand, soil and peat moss. Scratch a small raw place on the underside of the branch and dab on a little hormone powder, then bend the branch down into the hole and anchor it in place with a heavy wire arch. Firm down with soil and water well. Place a stone over the area to keep the soil above the branch undisturbed.

Give the new root-forming branch about 3 weeks and then check on its progress, gently scraping away a little of the soil. When good roots are established sever the stem from the parent plant and leave undisturbed for 3 days. Your new sturdy plant is now ready for transplanting to a preferred position. Prepare a hole with well-mixed soil and compost and place the plant in the hole, covering the roots with soil and pressing down well. Make a small dam around it and water well. Check twice a week to see that it does not dry out completely.

Root cuttings

Any plant that sends up suckers, for example *elder, soapwort*, the *mints, yarrow, bergamot, catnip, tarragon, asparagus, acanthus, ginger, iris, golden rod* and *lemon balm*, can easily be propagated. Select strong suckers and with a sharp spade chop off, taking as much root as possible. Have ready a deep seed box filled with light garden soil that has a little compost worked into it – 4 spades of soil to one spade of compost. Place the root cuttings horizontally into the box and cover with soil, firming down and watering well. Put the box in the shade, making sure that it is not in a draught, and cover with newspaper. Remember to keep the cuttings moist. When new growth and leaf buds appear, remove the covering and transplant into individual pots where the cuttings will develop into strong plants. Once they are established, plant out in the garden into well-prepared beds.

Root division

The best time to divide plants is autumn or early spring when the plants are not forming new growth. *Chives, strawberries, tarragon, golden rod, bergamot, origanum, creeping origanum, marjoram, ajuga, violet, acanthus, arum, lemon balm, buttercup, iris, sorrel, comfrey, tansy* and *yarrow* are amongst those plants that really divide well.

Dig out a clump and, placing 2 forks back to back with their prongs firmly in the clump, pull them apart and split the clump open. Then pull the sections into smaller sections and replant in newly prepared soil. Perennials such as these need fairly rich soil so dig in 3 spadefuls of compost and 2 of old manure to 1 square metre of garden soil. Keep the soil moist until the newly planted pieces have adjusted. Often the central portion or original mother plant will need to be discarded as it will have become woody and stunted.

If you replant into the original position, first dig in some compost and old manure as the soil may have become depleted.

Separate perennials every 2–3 years and give a yearly feed of compost and old manure. Perennials form the backbone of the herb garden so they deserve the best care.

5
HERBS TO ATTRACT BEES AND BUTTERFLIES

HERBS IN THE GARDEN THAT WILL ATTRACT BEES

Angelica	Dill	Rose
Borage	Eucomis	Rosemary
Chamomile	Lemon balm (melissa*)	Sour fig
Chives	Marigold	Strawberry
Columbine	Pineapple sage	Summer savory
Comfrey	Prickly pear	Water lily
Coriander	Rock-rose	

HERBS IN THE GARDEN THAT WILL ATTRACT BUTTERFLIES

Ajuga	Feverfew	Iris
Arum	Foxglove	Lavender
Basil	Garden valerian	Lemon verbena
Bergamot	Geranium – scented	Rosemary
Buttercup	Ginger	Tarragon
Catnip	Golden rod	Verbascum
Cornflower	Heliotrope	Vinca rosea
Dill	Hollyhock	Violet
Elder	Honeysuckle	Yarrow
Fennel	Hyssop	

*Melissa means 'little bee' and if the inside of a hive is rubbed with a handful of melissa leaves after the swarm has come the new swarm will never leave the hive.

6
FLOWERS IN THE HERB GARDEN

Many flowers, too, have their place in the herb garden, not only for man's pleasure but for use in his pain. These include the following:

Ajuga	Golden rod	Periwinkle
Alkanet	Heart's-ease pansy	Plumbago
Amaranthus	Heliotrope	Poppy
Arum	Holly	Rock-rose
Banksia rose	Hollyhock	Rose
Bergamot	Honeysuckle	Rose geranium
Broom	Hypericum	Soapwort
Calendula	Iris	Sunflower
Californian poppy	Jasmine	Tansy
Chamomile	Larkspur	Valerian – garden
Clove pink	Lavender	Verbascum
Columbine	Lemon verbena	Vinca
Cornflower	Marigold	Violet
Cotton lavender	Mignonette	White water lily
Forget-me-not	Morning glory	Yarrow
Foxglove	Myrtle	
Ginger	Nasturtium	

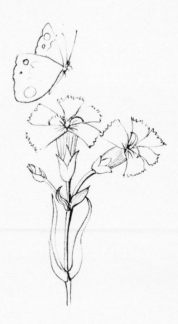

152

7
VEGETABLES AND FRUITS IN THE HERB GARDEN

VEGETABLES THAT HAVE THEIR PLACE IN THE HERB GARDEN

Asparagus	Chive	Parsnip
Cabbage	Lettuce	Pepper
Calabash	Lucerne	Potato
Carrot	Mealie	Pumpkin
Celery	Onion	Radish
Chicory	Parsley	

FRUITS THAT HAVE THEIR PLACE IN THE HERB GARDEN

Almond	Grape	Strawberry
Apple	Pawpaw	Walnut
Fig	Pomegranate	
Granadilla	Quince	

8
USEFUL WEEDS

Before pulling up those tiresome weeds in your herb garden, check to see whether they do not have their own special medicinal or culinary use – you may think twice about getting rid of them! The following are a few weeds worth encouraging and their uses are all discussed in *Margaret Roberts' Book of Herbs*.

Birdseed *Lepidium africanum*
Blackjack *Bidens pilosa*
Bladder hibiscus *Hibiscus trionum*
Blinkblaar *Ziziphus mucronata*
Chickweed *Stellaria media*
Cleavers *Galium aparine*
Cosmos *Cosmos bipinnatus*
Dandelion *Taraxacum officinale*
Dock *Rumex obtusifolius*
Donkey's peach *Araujia sericifera*
Fat hen *Chenopodium album*
Field bindweed *Convolvulus arvensis*
Field mallow *Malva*
Fleabane *Erigeron canadensis*
Groundsel *Senecio vulgaris*
Khakibos *Tagetes minuata*
Kweekgras *Cynodon dactylon*
Plantain *Plantago lanceolata major*
Pretoriabossie *Sida rhombifolia*
Purslane *Portulaca oleracea*
Shepherd's purse *Capsella bursa-pastoris*
Sow thistle *Sonchus olearceus*
Speedwell *Veronica officinalis*
Thorn apple *Datura stramonium*
Traveller's joy *Clematis virginica*
Tumbleweed *Boophane disticha*
Wandering jew *Commelina*

9
HOMEMADE GARDEN SPRAYS AND COMPOST MAKING

Home-brewed sprays are infinitely preferable to the powerful commercial chemical sprays on the market which are so harmful to all living things.

A general spray for aphids and other small plant pests
Combine equal quantities of *southernwood, khakibos, wormwood, tansy, wilde als* and, if you live at the sea, *seaweed* of any variety. Chop and steep in enough boiling water to cover and then strain. Add a cup of soap powder to a 5 litre (1 gallon) bucket of the brewed mixture, half a cup of mineral turpentine and 4 cups of sifted ash made from burned twigs, leaves and newspapers (the ash acts as a foliar feed). Splash or spray this brew onto the plants once a week to clear them of insect infestation. Repeat after rain.

A spray for roses
To 5 litres (1 gallon) water add the following:
5 ml (1 tsp) Sanpic for *rose beetles*
5 ml (1 tsp) Scrubbs ammonia for *red spider*
5 ml (1 tsp) Kelpak as a plant food
12,5 ml (1 tbls) grated blue mottle soap (to make the spray stick on the leaves and stems)
5 ml (1 tsp) Epsom salts to enable the ingredients to blend well

Mix first in one litre (4 cups) water, shake well to dissolve the soap, then add to the rest of the water and spray once a week on roses.

A spray for fruit flies and aphids
Chop equal quantities of *khakibos, marigold, tansy* and *basil* leaves. Place in a bucket of water, boil up for one hour, stand till cool and strain. To every 4 litres of water add 4 cups of sugar and 4 cups of ash made by burning leaves and twigs. The sugar helps to make the spray stick; it draws the fruit fly which feeds on the sugar solution and then dies. Spray onto peaches, tomatoes and apples.

A spray for rust on tomatoes
A strong brew can be made using equal quantities of *bitter bossie (klein khakibos)*, *dwarf marigold (Schkuhria pinnata)* and *prickly pear*. Chop up and cover with boiling water. Stand until cool, strain and spray onto tomatoes weekly. Repeat after rain.

A pick-me-up spray for ailing plants
Tea made from *chamomile* makes an excellent tonic spray. Soak 2 handfuls of flowers

in 1 litre (4 cups) boiling water overnight, strain and use as a spray.

Another general spray for ailing plants can be made by boiling up 4 handfuls of *sage* in 5 litres (1 gallon) water. Leave to stand overnight, then strain and spray.

A spray for apple scab and powdery mildew
Take 2 handfuls chopped *chives* to 1 litre (4 cups) water, boil up, strain and spray onto apples to prevent apple scab, or onto squashes and cucumbers to prevent powdery mildew.

A spray for potato and tomato blight
A strong tea made from chopped *garlic* and *onions* can be used as a spray for blight on potatoes and tomatoes. Chop 2 bulbs garlic and 4 large onions, boil with 3 litres (12 cups) water, cool and strain. Use as a spray shortly after preparation.

A spray against plant bacteria
Boil up 3 parts chopped *rue*, 1 part *marigolds* and 1 part *hyssop* in enough water to cover. Strain and use as a spray for affected plants.

A spray to encourage wilt and rust resistance in plants
Boil up several handfuls of *valeriana* leaves, using enough water to cover them. Cool and strain, then spray onto the soil or directly onto plants at any stage.

Comfrey liquid fertilizer
Comfrey liquid fertilizer is made by taking an old metal drum or plastic garbage container of about 45 litres (10 gallons) capacity and packing it half full with large comfrey leaves. Then fill the container to the brim with water and leave it to soak for 3 weeks, until the leaves have rotted down. This stock liquid is mixed 50/50 with water and poured around the roots of the plants.

The comfrey liquid can be used for pot-plants if it is greatly diluted. I have found that about 25 ml (1 fl oz) of the stock solution added to 4,5 litres (1 gallon) water makes a nourishing mixture. Regular application of this liquid, plus plenty of sunlight and love will make your indoor plants thrive.

COMPOST MAKING

If you are a good compost maker you will be a successful organic gardener and herb grower! Compost is the very heart of the organic method of gardening – ie using only natural substances to increase the growth and vitality of your plants – and compost is the base for your herb garden. Perhaps a good definition of compost would be to describe this rich black magic as a substance which gives fertility to the soil and thus productivity to the plants grown in that soil. Another advantage that compost has is that it helps maintain the moisture content of the soil and in our drought prone country this is a necessity.

Basically, to make your own compost pile at almost no cost is not difficult. Every potato peeling, grass clipping, raked leaf or pulled up weed, and any manure that you have at hand can be thrown into the compost pile. First build it, then moisten it, turn it a few times and forget it! Some weeks later spade it over and smell the dark richness of converted kitchen waste and weeds and you will never again use any other kind of compost.

Structure and method

Dave Rosenberg, the best compost-maker I know and chairman of the Organic Soil Association, taught me his 'no fail' method which he has allowed me to share with you. The simplicity and practicality of his method means that compost making can be easily integrated into our daily living.

Firstly, the site you choose should be a small corner about 2 metres by 2 metres in size where the heap can mature for 2–3 weeks undisturbed. I find that loosening clay or turf-type soil with a fork before you begin seems to aid the aeration of the heap, but on sandy soil this is not necessary. A rough bed of coarse garden material can be laid down – or, if available, cabbage and mealie stalks, soft prunings, coarse veld grass and dead flower stalks. The aim is to allow air to get into the heap from the base. Then a mixture of garden residue, kitchen waste, lawn clippings, weeds, crushed eggshells is moistened and mixed with a good sprinkling of manure and packed on top of this base.

Use a soft sprinkling of water all the time while making and packing onto the heap. Tread the heap down now and then while building it up but do not make it too soggy. After packing a layer of your mixture about 15 cm deep spread a thin layer of manure and stable bedding over the layer of this mixture. The manure and stable bedding act as activators and so do the outer leaves of cabbage and cauliflower, as well as free-range chicken manure. (Do not use manure from chicken batteries as it may contain ingredients harmful to humans; do not use it on food crops either.)

Cover the manure layer with a thin layer of soil mixed with some woodash, dolomitic lime and rock phosphate if you can obtain them. Repeat the 15 cm layers – plant refuse, kitchen waste, manure and soil – over and over, moistening with a fine spray nozzle on the hose and stamping down until you have a heap 1–1,5 metres high. Top it with a 25 mm thick layer of garden soil and then cover the heap with veld grass to maintain the moisture and to keep off the sun. In very wet areas, such as the Cape winter rainfall area, cover with black plastic sheeting to maintain the warmth and to keep the pile from becoming sodden.

Air circulation is an important element in the compost heap. In larger heaps a post or pipe can be driven into the ground at the centre or several posts driven in at various points in the heap. When you have finished building the heap remove the post or pipe to create a ventilation hole. You will be amazed at the degree of heat that builds up in the heap.

About two and a half to three weeks later comes the next important step. This is the turning of the heap. Turn and mix thoroughly and remoisten, as in the initial heating up of the heap there is a marked moisture loss. In South Africa's heat and dryness it is essential to maintain that moisture. The heat build-up reaches 71°–77°C in those first 7–10 days and this is the secret of success. It is a sign of much activity within the heap of the decomposing of material.

Properly made compost has a pleasant odour at all times and does not present a health hazard. Decaying matter which is too wet and without aeration is anaerobic or foul-smelling and is a deterrent to compost making.

Seaweed, liquid manure or liquid seaweed – provided that none of these is chemically made or preserved – can also be added to the heap and will add essential and beneficial trace elements. In fact, anything that is natural and decomposable is an acceptable addition.

I have two kitchen bins at hand, one for plastic, tins, wrappings etc, and the other for peelings, vegetable pips, outer leaves and fruit skins. Having a separate bin means a quick and effortless daily addition to the pile.

Several compost bins and receptacles are available at garden and hardware shops and it is often useful to have smaller heaps going all the time. Remember that the larger the heap the greater the retention of temperature. A very successful compost can be made in the small bins for the smaller garden. The greatest compost enemies are excessive moisture and excessive dryness. Should your heap become too dry, dismantle it and sprinkle with water with a fine hose. Repack the layers, watering each one well, but not so well as to become sodden.

Undoubtedly the best fertilizer there is, is a good compost. It contains no harmful substances and can be easily assimilated by the soil where earthworms and micro-organisms act upon it and convert it into the humus on which plants feed.

Mulching

Mulching and compost making go hand in hand. Many home gardeners are not fully aware of the benefits of mulching but without it weeds grow abundantly and vigorously and the soil rapidly dries out – a very real problem in this country with its periods of water shortages and restrictions. Surface evaporation is prevented when the beds are covered with a 5 cm layer of mulch. At the same time the mulching material is rotting and being incorporated into the soil by worms and other soil inhabitants and the fertility of the soil is thus being maintained.

If you are short of compost, mulching is the next best soil saver and in the blazing summer heat it is necessary to conserve coolness as well as moisture.

Mulching materials abound in every garden. They include fallen leaves (roughly chopped), stalks, twigs, weeds and grass clippings. (Do not use grass clippings in a green or cut state as they tend to pack and become sour; in ant-infested areas they also provide a wonderful home for a colony.) Mix grass clippings with leaves and twigs and chips of bark and even rough sawdust. I find chopped dried khakibos is a wonderful insect repellent and I add it to the mulching materials to keep everything sweet-smelling and ant-free. Exact quantities do not really matter and your own experimenting and experience will give you the best results for your area.

In black turf soils I find digging in the mulch to be more beneficial but on sandy soils I lay the mulch on top and get better results.

A friend in a suburban garden used shredded newspaper and lawn clippings around her roses, with a sprinkling of dried tansy leaves as an insect repellent. She grew wonderful specimens, often winning places in the local flower shows.

Whatever you use, however, mulching will become a vital part of gardening and in the herb garden it will be of great benefit – so save all those fallen leaves (particularly sage as it is a natural fertilizer) and enjoy a weed-free garden!

10
COMPANION PLANTING

An excellent reason for growing herbs in our gardens, apart from their culinary, fragrance or medicinal uses, is that the scents of certain herbs actually help protect other plants against insects. For example, a row of cabbages interplanted with a row of marigolds suffers far less insect damage than if planted alone. The fragrance of the marigold, pungent and strong, confuses and repels the egg-laying moths.

Annual herbs such as coriander, anise and mustard, are protective herbs interplanted between rows of vegetables, and seem to aid one another's growth too. Special attention should be paid, therefore, to the layout of a vegetable garden.

Plants having complementary physical demands can be grouped together – eg moisture and shade loving plants can be placed beside taller, non-moisture loving plants, and a pleasing garden can be landscaped bearing such companion planting in mind.

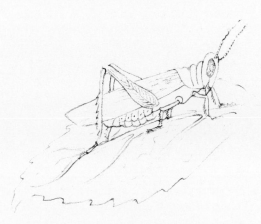

COMPANIONATE ALPHABET

ANISE (*Pimpinella anisum*)
Grow anise with coriander; seed germination is more successful.

APPLE TREE (*Malus*)
Ring chives around the stem.

APRICOT TREE (*Prunus armeniaca*)
Ring nasturtiums around the stem.

ASPARAGUS (*Asparagus officinalis*)
Interplant asparagus with tomatoes and parsley.

BASIL (*Ocimum basilicum*)
Do not plant near rue (sweet and bitter do not go well together!)

BEANS (*Phaseolus* and *Vicia*)
Beans thrive near carrots and cauliflower.
Beans and beetroot also like each other.
Beans are inhibited by onions and garlic.
Plant with mealies as a quick trellis for runner-beans once the mealie plant is near-
    ing maturity.
Broad beans interplanted with potatoes and marigolds do well.
Bush beans grow well with celery planted in a ratio of 6 plants celery to 1 plant
    beans.
Keep beans and fennel far apart.
Beans grow well with strawberries.

BEETROOT (*Beta vulgaris*)
Beetroot likes to grow near dwarf beans, onions and kohlrabi.
Lettuce and cabbage like beetroot.

BORAGE (*Borago officinalis*)
Borage and strawberries thrive together.
Bees love borage.

BUTTERCUP (*Ranunculus multifidus*)
All members of the *Ranunculus* family are voracious feeders so try to confine them.

160

CHAMOMILE (*Matricaria recutita*)
Chamomile helps onions – ratio of 1 chamomile plant to every 4 metres of onions.

CARAWAY (*Carum carvi*)
Caraway is a good companion to green peas.
Freshly gathered seeds, when baked into a loaf, help indigestion in heavy breads.
Caraway also helps digest cheese dishes.

CARROT (*Daucus carota*)
Carrots grow happily between rows of lettuce, chives and radishes.
The carrot fly is unsettled with rosemary, sage and wormwood. If these cannot be
    grown near the rows of carrots, crushed, dried leaves of any of the three may be
    sprinkled around the carrots to deter the carrot fly.

CASTOR OIL PLANT (*Ricinus communis*)
This poisonous plant repels mosquitoes but *should be cultivated with caution.*
It encourages pumpkins to set fruit and makes a good screen behind the vegetable
    or herb garden.

CAULIFLOWER (*Brassica oleracea botrytis*)
Cauliflower grows well near celery and celery helps keep away the cabbage moths
    that attack all brassicas.

CELERY (*Apium graveolens*)
Celery will benefit from leeks growing nearby.
Tomatoes are good neighbours, as are bush beans.

CHERVIL (*Anthriscus cerefolium*)
Chervil grows well if radishes are somewhere nearby, but needs shade.

CHIVES (*Allium schoenoprasum*)
Good near apple trees.

CITRUS (*Citrus*)
All citrus trees do better with a guava tree in the vicinity, and the protective in-
    fluence of an oak tree or a rubber tree.

COMFREY (*Symphytum officinale*)
Comfrey is beneficial to all surrounding plants as it brings up rich trace elements in
    the soil by its deep rooting system and provides moisture, shade and shelter to
    other plants grown nearby.
It is invaluable on the compost heap.

CORIANDER (*Coriandrum sativum*)
Coriander hinders the seed formation in fennel but when sown with anise helps the
    latter to germinate.
Bees are drawn into the garden when coriander is in bloom.

CORNFLOWER (*Centaurea cyanus*)
The cornflower helps the grain seed formation in oat and wheat fields.

DANDELION (*Taraxacum officinale*)
This garden weed, with its wide variety of medicinal uses, also exhales a gas, ethy-
lene, which inhibits the height or growth of plants nearby.
The dandelion helps flowers and fruit of neighbouring plants to mature early.
Dandelions have a happy companionship with lucerne.

DILL (*Peucedanum graveolens*)
Dill is good with cabbages but has a strong inhibiting effect on carrots and tomatoes
even if sown in the ratio of 20 plants to 1 dill plant. Pull it out or cut back before it
goes into bloom to prevent this effect.

ELDER (*Sambucus nigra*)
Grow elder near compost areas as it has a beneficial effect on the humus beneath the
leaves; can be added to the compost heap or dug into the topsoil.

EUPHORBIA (*Spurge*) 400 species
These troublesome weeds are in actual fact friends as they protect tender plants of
other species by fostering a soil which preserves warmth.

FAT HEN (*Chenopodium album*)
This lush weed growing in the potato field is an indication that the soil is tired of
growing potatoes! It also indicates a good humus-fermented soil however.

FENNEL (*Foeniculum vulgare*)
Fennel is harmful to bush beans, cucumber, tomatoes, kohlrabi and caraway.
Fennel suffers when planted near wormwood.

FOXGLOVE (*Digitalis purpurea*)
Foxgloves give an invigorating effect to other plants near them and seem to stimu-
late their growth.
They grow well near pine trees.
To make cut foxgloves last well indoors, add 2 cupfuls of tea to the water in the vase.

GARLIC (*Allium sativum*)
Grow garlic between roses but it will inhibit the growth of peas and beans.
Pieces of garlic in stored wheat and mealie bins will keep them insect free.

GRAPES (*Vitis* and *Muscadinia*)
A vine supported by or grown near a mulberry tree will grow well.
The yield of grapes is increased by planting hyssop nearby.

HORSERADISH (*Amoracia rusticana*)
Horseradish has a helpful effect on potatoes if grown around the edges of the patch.
Dig up horseradish after each season or it will spread abundantly.
Grated root bottled with hot vinegar, is a delicious condiment.

162

HYSSOP (*Hyssopus officinalis*)

Hyssop attracts the cabbage butterfly and lures it away from the cabbage patch, so a border of hyssop is a useful edging to the vegetable garden.

It encourages the setting of fruit in grapevines.

KHAKIBOS (*Tagetes minuata*)

Every khakibos plant should be gathered and used for its insect-repellent properties.

It keeps insects away and can be allowed to grow between lettuces, cabbages and tomatoes.

Crushed leaves under tomatoes that are ripening help prevent rot where they touch the ground.

Khakibos is beneficial to beans.

Dried leaves are an insecticide so sprinkle freely amongst vegetables.

LAVENDER (*Lavendula*)

Lavender is a moth repellent and grows happily near scented geraniums, each enhancing the other's perfume.

Lavender will also grow well near or interspersed with legumes.

LEEK (*Allium porrum*)

Leeks and celery help each other sown in alternate rows.

Leeks also like celeriac and are aided by carrots, and they help to repel carrot fly.

LEMON BALM (*Melissa officinalis*)

Melissa radiates a beneficent atmosphere to its surrounding plants.

Grown in pastures it will aid the milk flow in cows.

When a new swarm comes to a hive, rub the inside of the hive with a handful of melissa and the swarm will never leave it.

MARIGOLD (*Tagetes* species)

Marigolds are the best treatment for nematodes in the soil for their roots excrete a substance which kills them.

Grown between rows of tomatoes they seem to increase the yield of fruit.

Marigold flowers and foliage make a wonderful insect repellent and grown interspersed all over the garden will effectively keep insects away all summer long.

MARJORAM (*Oreganum vulgare*)

Marjoram and its cousin origanum are beneficent plants to their neighbours without exception and as such are indispensable in the garden and vegetable garden.

MEALIE (*Zea mays*)

Grow mealies amongst potatoes in alternate rows and as a support for beans.

Pumpkins, melons and squash also benefit from the mealies' shade and shelter and each benefits the other's soil requirements.

MINT (*Mentha*)

The mints help control aphids on nearby vegetation.

163

To repel ants chop and sprinkle mint around their holes.
To keep flies away hang bunches of bruised mint in the house and to keep flies off a milk cow rub handfuls of mint or spearmint leaves over her every day.

MUSTARD (*Brassica alba*)
This fast-growing annual is a help to fruit trees and grape vines if grown nearby.
A crop of mustard, dug in and allowed to stand for a season, will restore the general health of a poor, over-mineralised soil.

NASTURTIUM (*Tropaeolum majus*)
Planted near broccoli, nasturtium keeps it free from aphids.
Planted under apple trees, it keeps woolly aphids away.

NETTLE (*Urtica dioica*)
The stinging nettle stimulates the formation of humus in the soil – the leaves and stem rot to an ideal humus and the secretions around its roots stimulate growth in other plants.
It changes the chemical processes in nearby plants, eg grown near marjoram and sage it increases their essential oil content.
Nettle helps plants around it, eg tomato plants, to grow more resistant to spoiling.
Nettle strengthens and invigorates all plants grown around it and can be used to make a useful fermented extract which acts as a manure. Cut down several nettle plants and cover with water. Leave to decompose for three weeks, then use as a manure or strain and use as a spray to help plants overcome drought conditions, or to strengthen ailing plants and improve their general health.

OAK (*Quercus*)
An oak is beneficent to other trees; citrus trees in particular like an oak tree as protection.
Oak leaf mulch is valuable when spread between plants as it is a repellent for slugs, snails and cutworms.

ONIONS (*Allium cepa*)
Onions grow well with beetroot, while their own growth is helped by chamomile – 1 chamomile plant to every 4 metres of onion plants.
Alternate rows of carrots and onions will protect the carrots from carrot fly.
Onion juice is soothing when applied to wasp and bee stings.

PARSLEY (*Petroselinum crispum*)
Try growing parsley between roses or in a circle around their base. Not only is it a charming edging or border, but it attracts bees and remains green and attractive for two seasons, growing well even if picked continuously.
It is also a good companion to tomatoes as they enhance one another's growth and flavour.

PEAS (*Pisum sativum*)
Grow peas and radishes, carrots, cucumbers, beans, mealies and turnips near each other.

164

Plant peas far away from onions, chives and shallots.

If peas and potatoes are grown in alternate rows, the potatoes do well from the nitrogen given off by the roots of the pea.

Do not plant peas two years in succession in the same ground.

PENNYROYAL (*Mentha pulegium*)

Pennyroyal is an ant and mosquito repellent. Sprinkle round ants' nests; rub onto pillows and arms and face to repel mosquitoes. Edge vegetable beds with pennyroyal so that it can be walked on to release the oils.

PEPPERMINT (*Mentha piperita*)

Plant peppermint between cabbages to protect them from the cabbage butterfly.

Edge paths with peppermint as it can be walked on and its fragrance can be most beneficial and refreshing to a weary gardener.

PINE (*Pinus* species)

If strawberries are mulched by pine needles, the mulch increases their fruit production and adds flavour to the fruit. It also makes a clean 'straw' on which the berries can rest.

Pine needles inhibit the germination of seeds and pine trees suppress the growth of wheat.

PLANTAIN (*Plantago* species)

Red clover and plantain grow well together.

Plantain plants, before setting flowers, make a wonderful addition to the compost heap as a green manure.

PYRETHRUM (*Chrysanthemum cinerarifolium*)

The flowers of pyrethrum are used in pesticide sprays but planted as a border to the vegetable or herb garden they protect many plants from insect infestation.

They are particularly good alongside strawberries, helping to keep the berries pest free.

RADISH (*Raphanus sativus*)

Radishes are beneficial to many vegetables.

Peas and radishes are mutually helpful.

The flavour of radishes grown near nasturtiums is wonderfully enhanced.

Lettuce grown near radishes makes the latter tender.

Chervil and radish encourage in each other invigorated growth and flavour.

Grow a row of radishes near runner beans and cucumbers to help keep away beetles.

Do not grow radish near hyssop as they seem to dislike one another.

ROSEMARY (*Rosmarinus officinalis*)

Sage and rosemary are happy companions.

Rosemary repels carrot fly.

Rosemary keeps evil spirits away, so a rosemary bush grown in each corner of the garden will ensure adequate protection!

ROSES (*Rosa* species)

Roses do well with parsley and also with garlic. In fact roses which are grown near
garlic have a deeper perfume. A compost made from onion and garlic refuse helps
keep rose beetles away.

Mignonette grows well round rose bushes and here, too, the fragrance of both mignonette and the roses will become stronger.

RUE (*Ruta graveolens*)

Do not grow rue and sweet basil together.

Keep rue as a border plant behind the vegetable garden and around compost areas,
stables and chicken runs to repel flies.

SAGE (*Salvia officinalis*)

Sage and rosemary stimulate one another.

Sage drops its leaves and combined with wood-ash and manure, they make an
amazing fertilizer, especially for grapevines.

Sage is a plant tonic so never waste a leaf! It seems to stimulate whichever plants
grow around it.

SALSIFY (Oyster plant) (*Tragopogon porrifolius*)

Salsify helps carrots grow prolifically and repels the carrot fly even better than do
garlic and onions.

SANTOLINA (Cotton lavender) (*Santolina chamaecyparissus*)

Grow santolina between lettuce and spinach as an insect repellent; crush a few
leaves as you work amongst the plants. Use in sachets with other insect-repelling
herbs. Sprays of santolina placed behind books will help repel fish-moths.

SAVORY – SUMMER (*Satureja (Satureia) hortensis*)

If summer savory is grown around onions as a border it greatly increases their
growth.

It is also helpful to green beans, aiding their flower development and adding to their
flavour.

SAVORY – WINTER (*Satureja montana*)

Winter savory is an insect repellent and can be grown as an edging to the garden.

It inhibits the germination of seeds so do not grow it near seed beds.

SOAPWORT (*Saponaria officinalis*)

The saponin-rich soapwort appears to work beneficially on crops which mature in
the ground. Saponin is a plant glycoside, a soap-like substance which occurs in
various plant families. The humifying remains of these plants benefit the succes-
sional plants.

Other saponin-producing plants besides soapwort are: spinach, tomatoes, runner
beans, potatoes, violas, mullein (verbascum) and some carnation varieties. *Saponaria officinalis*, however, is probably the most well known. It can be a pest in the
garden but once it is established perhaps it is worth keeping for its many useful
qualities.

166

SOUTHERNWOOD (*Artemisia abrotanum*)
Southernwood protects cabbages from aphids and is a general insect repellent.
Southernwood sprays placed between books and in cupboards will deter fish-
    moths.
Planted near fruit trees, it will repel fruit fly and night-feeding fruit moths.

SPEARMINT (*Mentha spicata*)
Rodents do not like spearmint. Bunches of spearmint and khakibos can be hung in
    store-rooms to deter rats.
It repels ants when sprinkled around ant holes.
Grown near vegetables, spearmint will help control aphids.

SUNFLOWER (*Helianthus annuus*)
Potatoes and sunflowers stunt one another's growth.
Seeds from the sunflower are one way of persuading birds to visit your garden and
    bees love its nectar and pollen.
Cucumber grows well near sunflowers.

SWEET BASIL (*Ocimum basilicum*)
Never grow sweet basil near rue – they are harmful to each other and must be kept as
    far apart as possible.

TANSY (*Tanacetum vulgare*)
Tansy is an insect-repellent plant and, planted between the trees, is good for keep-
    ing fruit fly and fruit moths away from peaches.

THYME (*Thymus vulgaris*)
Thyme has a fragrant oil, thymol, which helps repel aphids and moths.
It has an enlivening effect on its neighbouring plants and makes a good protective
    border to the vegetable garden.

VALERIAN (*Centranthus ruber*)
Grown as a border plant it is beneficent to most vegetables.
It stimulates phosphorus activity in the soil in its vicinity and attracts earthworms.
It also attracts cats, which love its bruised roots.

WOOD ASH (burnt twigs, branches, stems, leaves of all kinds)
Not a herb but important enough to be included here as it is made from vegetable
    matter.
Every precious ounce of this wonderful plant food should be carefully gathered up.
It is an excellent tonic to dig in around fruit trees.
Sprinkled around vegetables, especially root vegetables, it is a wonderful fertiliser
    and deters insect pests.
Just a small handful placed around plants maintains soil moisture and provides the
    soil with minerals.

WORMWOOD (*Artemisia absinthium*)
Wormwood is a general inhibitor of plants as its root secretions are toxic. It contains

a toxic substance called absinthum and when rain flows over the leaves this soluble substance is washed out into the ground where it remains active for some time. Do not, therefore, grow wormwood close to other plants.

YARROW (*Achillea millefolium*)
Yarrow is helpful to most vegetables, grown as a border plant. It does not mind being trampled so it can be grown alongside paths and, itself a good medicinal herb, it is a good companion to all medicinal herbs.

11
INSECT-REPELLING PLANTS

Insect	Repelling Plant	How to Use
ANTS	garlic	Pound 4 garlic bulbs. To 4 litres water add 250 ml (1 cup) washing powder and the crushed garlic. Mix and pour into holes.
	khakibos	Dried, powdered and sprinkled around holes.
	mints	Chopped and sprinkled around holes.
	pennyroyal	Dried, powdered and sprinkled around holes.
	southernwood	Dried, powdered and sprinkled around holes.
	spearmint	Fresh, chopped and sprinkled around holes.
	tansy	Dried, powdered and sprinkled around holes.
APHIDS	mints	Grow nearby.
	nasturtium	Grow between plants.
	nettle	Grow nearby.
	khakibos rue tansy wormwood	Combination of two or three of these plants. For example chop and boil 1 handful each of khakibos, rue and tansy. To 2 litres (8 cups) boiled water add 250 ml (1 cup) soap powder and the above herb mixture. Strain and use as a spray.

Insect	Repelling Plant	How to Use
CABBAGE MOTHS, WORM	marigold rosemary sage thyme wormwood	Plant between rows of cabbages and other brassicas.
CUTWORM	oak	Mulch leaves thickly around plants.
FISH-MOTHS	lavender cloves	Fill bags with crushed cloves and lavender. Add a little lavender oil.
	rue	Dried and powdered, placed between books.
	santolina	Place fresh sprays in cupboards; replace sprays from time to time.
	southernwood	Fresh sprays tucked between books. Change monthly.
FLIES	basil	Fresh green leaves in a bowl indoors.
	nettles	Hang a bunch of fresh nettles in the kitchen. (Pick with gloves on.)
	rue	Dried or fresh in bowls around a room.
	tansy	Dried, crushed and sprinkled.
	tomato	Fresh green sprays of leaves indoors; bruise from time to time.
	wormwood	Dried, crushed and sprinkled.
FRUIT FLY	cayenne pepper chillies	Sprinkle cayenne pepper or ground cayenne chillies on leaves and around trees.
	tansy	Plant thickly under peach trees.
MOSQUITOES	legumes	As a crop.
	marigold pennyroyal	Rub onto skin and pillows.

Insect	Repelling Plant	How to Use
	rosemary southernwood	Sprays in a vase in the room; bruise leaves from time to time.
MOTHS	khakibos	Dried and powdered, put into cupboards and along skirting boards.
POTATO BEETLES	eggplant (brinjal)	Interplant.
	green beans	Interplant.
	khakibos	Dried and powdered, sprinkled around plants.
	marigolds	Interplant.
SLUGS	oak	Leaf mulch.
WEEVILS	garlic	Cloves, slightly crushed, in food containers.
WOOLLY APHIDS	nasturtiums	Plant near broccoli, cabbages etc.
	tansy	Use in spray with soapy water.

171

12
COUNTRY REMEDIES

This is a small collection of natural, easily applied remedies, all of which have stood the test of time. These are the remedies our forefathers relied on and which have all but been forgotten, the comforting, soothing aids that ease the conditions and soothe the pain.

Never use these remedies to replace standard medical treatment, however, in a case of serious illness, although none of these cures will harm and many will surprise you with their efficacy and speedy relief. Of course some may not do as much good as you hope – but all are worth a try!

ASTHMA AND CHEST COLDS

CHEST COLD AND ASTHMA SYRUP

3 garlic bulbs, peeled
625 ml (2½ cups) water
185 ml (1¼ cups) cider vinegar
100 g (½ cup) sugar or honey

Chop the peeled garlic cloves and simmer in the water until the liquid is reduced by half. Remove the garlic by straining through a sieve and then add the other ingredients and boil to a syrup-like consistency. Place the garlic in a bottle and then cover with the syrup. One dessert-spoon of mixture, including the pieces of garlic, to be taken each night.

BOILS

BOIL POULTICE

12,5 ml (1 tbls) honey
12,5 ml (1 tbls) castor oil

Warm honey and castor oil together and spread on a clean piece of lint. Place on afflicted area and wrap it with a towel which has been wrung out in hot water (this will keep the heat in). Alternatively, hold in place with a castor oil leaf that has been warmed in hot water. Change dressing frequently.

172

HOT ONION BOIL POULTICE

Roast a whole onion in a slow oven, then cut it in half and apply to the boil. Bind in place – but take care that it is not so hot as to burn the already inflamed skin.

POTATO POULTICE

Wash, peel and grate a fresh potato. Apply to the afflicted area and keep in place with a dressing. It will become warm as it draws out the inflammation and when this happens discard and replace with another freshly grated potato.

This soothing remedy can also be used for swellings, sores and minor burns.

BURNS AND SCALDS

Cut a raw potato in half and apply immediately, squeezing the juice onto the painful area. Then apply a thick smearing of honey to exclude all air and cover with a bandage. Keep in position for 24 hours, then inspect the burn and reapply if necessary.

The inside of a ripe banana skin is also effective, bound in place and changed every few hours.

*See also *Potato Poultice* under BOILS

CONVALESCENCE

CONVALESCENT BROTH

This is also an excellent remedy for babies with gastro-intestinal infections.

260 g (½ cup) wheat (whole grain)
400 g (½ cup) oats (non-instant)
400 g (½ cup) barley
750 ml (3 cups) water
a little honey

Grind the grains together in a pestle and mortar. Boil up in the water for half an hour. Add honey, and drink 125 ml (½ cup) 3 times a day.

CORNS

CORN CURES

Soak an ivy leaf overnight in vinegar, then wrap it over the corn. Repeat daily for ten days.

Place a piece of fresh garlic on a bandage and bind in position over the corn. Renew every day for ten days.

Wrap a strip of pineapple peel around the corn, also renewing daily for ten days or until the corn disappears.

A slice of lemon bound on overnight for several nights also works well.

COUGHS AND COLDS

GUM TREE INHALANT

250 ml (1 cup) boiling water
a few drops oil of eucalyptus

Pour boiling water into a basin and add oil. Lean over the basin, cover the head with a towel and inhale the fumes. Keep the eyes tightly closed and inhale for 10 minutes.

SUNFLOWER COUGH SYRUP

125 ml (½ cup) sunflower seeds
1¼ litres (5 cups) water
50 g (¼ cup) sugar
190 ml (¾ cup) gin

Boil sunflower seeds in water until reduced to 500 ml (2 cups) water. Add sugar and gin. Store in a sealed bottle.
  Dosage: 5–10 ml (1–2 tsp) 3 or 4 times a day.

HOT LEMON AND HONEY DRINK FOR COLDS

Squeeze half a lemon into 250 ml (1 cup) boiling water. Mix in 12 ml (1 dessertsp) honey. Add a dash of brandy and sip, inhaling the steam.

COUGH MIXTURE

37,5 ml (3 tbls) honey
25 ml (2 tbls) lemon juice

Mix well and use to relieve a persistent cough, taking 5 ml (1 tsp) at a time.
  This is particularly good for children as it is a safe cough cure and they can take it frequently.

*See also *Pick-me-up Tonic* under GENERAL TONICS

CRAMP

CRAMP CURES

For a painful muscular cramp in the leg, bind the leg with fresh periwinkle (*Vinca major*) strands, leaving on the leaves and flowers.

Alternatively, quickly put a pinch of salt on the tongue.

DISINFECTANT

ONION DISINFECTANT

Slice an onion and place it in a sickroom and it will absorb all the germs from the air. Replace daily with fresh slices and burn the old ones.

EARACHE

EARACHE BAG

10 cloves
1 stick cinnamon
1 grated nutmeg
2 leaves mace

Crush ingredients together. Sew into a small muslin bag and heat in a low oven. Apply this little bag to the painful area, holding it in place a few minutes. Warm it up again and keep applying until the pain eases. The bag is as effective a treatment for toothache too.

EYES

CUCUMBER EYE LOTION

For soothing inflamed, tired eyes squeeze the juice from a 15 cm slice of fresh cucumber, add 25 ml (2 tbls) milk and apply to the eyes internally and externally. (The juice can also be applied without the milk.) It will cool and soothe the eyes and tone up the membranes.

CLOVE EYE LOTION

Boil up 5 cloves in 250 ml (1 cup) water and use as an eye wash. Alternatively, soak pads of cotton wool in the lotion and rest with the pads over the eyes.

EYE BATH

5 ml (1 tsp) honey
250 ml (1 cup) boiled water

Add honey to the boiling water and simmer for 5 minutes. Cool. Bathe the eyes 2 or 3 times daily, or soak cotton wool pads in the brew, place them over the eyes and relax for a while.

FEVERS

FEVER CURE
400 g (2 cups) pearl barley

2,5 litres (10 cups) water
juice of 1 lemon
honey

Simmer barley in the water. Strain and cool. Add lemon juice and honey to taste. Drink continuously throughout the day and the fever will subside. It will also help general chestiness.

APPLE DRINK FOR FEVER

3 apples
1 litre (4 cups) boiling water
honey

Core and slice apples without peeling and boil up in the water. Mash apples through a plastic sieve and throw out skins. Stir in honey to taste. Allow to cool and take as often as required. This is also an effective remedy for stomach upsets.

FEVER VINEGAR

20 elderflower heads
625 ml (2½ cups) apple cider vinegar, warmed

Pack the flowers into a jar and pour over the warm vinegar, pressing the heads down well. Seal and stand for 10 days, shaking the jar daily. Then sieve through muslin and store in a well-corked bottle.

Dilute with a little water and drink throughout the day to bring down a fever. It can also be used as a gargle for a sore throat.

GENERAL TONICS

LAVENDER TONIC LOTION

25 ml (2 tbls) dried lavender flowers
10 ml (2 tsp) crushed cinnamon
1 grated nutmeg
12,5 ml (1 tbls) rosemary leaves
1 bottle pure cane spirit

Pulverize all the ingredients and mix well together. Add bottle of cane spirit. Stand the mixture in the sunlight and shake well once a day for a week. Strain, bottle and cork well. Use on cloths wrung out in cold water and placed over the forehead for headaches, fevers and nervousness; also apply to the pulse on the wrists.

TONIC FOOD: HOMEMADE MUESLI

This complete food contains all your daily mineral, vitamin and bulk requirements. Serve with warm milk, yoghurt, fresh fruit and honey.

1 kg (2 lb) oats (the large flake type)
800 g (5 cups) bran
500 g almonds and pecan nuts
200 g sunflower seeds

1 kg (2 lb) dried fruit, mixed and finely chopped

Chop the fruit and nuts into small pieces, mix all ingredients together and store in the refrigerator. Eat 3–6 tablespoons daily.

OAT GRUEL FOR RESTORING ENERGY AND BODY BUILDING

400 g (2 cups) oats (non-instant)
2 litres (8 cups) water
25 ml (2 tbls) honey

Boil oats in the water, strain and stir in the honey. This is a soothing, warming, somewhat glutinous drink but if taken daily for one month will produce excellent results. As a fortifier for pre-examination nerves it is a wonderful aid.

PICK-ME-UP TONIC

50 g (¼ cup) sugar
625 ml (2½ cups) dry sherry
62,5 ml (5 tbls) rosewater
5 ml (1 tsp) nutmeg
12,5 ml (1 tbls) cinnamon bark, slightly crushed

Warm all ingredients together, pour into a bottle and stand for one month. Strain through muslin and re-bottle. Take a small sherry glass each evening to restore spirits and energy.

When you feel a cold coming on this is a wonderfully soothing warmer. Heat the tonic in a cup by standing it in boiling water. Add a squeeze of lemon juice and sip slowly.

GOUT

GOUT CURE

1 handful pennyroyal mint
juice of one medium sized onion (extracted in a garlic press)
250 ml (1 cup) boiling water

Pour boiling water over the pennyroyal and stand for 20 minutes. Strain and add the onion juice. Dip a piece of lint into this decoction and wrap it around the afflicted area.

Including garlic and onion in your diet will also help this painful affliction.

HAIR

HAIR TONIC AND SETTING LOTION

250 ml (1 cup) sage leaves, cut up
250 ml (1 cup) rosemary leaves, cut up
600 ml (1 pt) water

Place sage and rosemary leaves in a saucepan and pour over 600 ml (1 pt) water. Bring to the boil and simmer for 3 minutes, keeping covered. Cool and stand for 3 hours and then strain the liquid. Massage the liquid into the scalp each night.

HAIR GROWING OIL

250 ml (1 cup) maidenhair fern
250 ml (1 cup) willow leaves
3 cloves
500 ml (2 cups) olive oil

Combine all ingredients, place in a pot and heat slowly by standing the pot in a bigger pot of hot water over a low heat. Keep heating for one hour and then allow to cool. Strain when cold and pour into a glass jar. Massage a little of this oil into the scalp every night.

HAIR TONIC

75 g (3 oz) nasturtium leaves
75 g (3 oz) nasturtium seeds
75 g (3 oz) nasturtium flowers
75 g (3 oz) young nettle leaves
600 ml (1 pt) pure cane spirit
few drops rosemary oil or
3 thumb-length sprays of rosemary

Mince herbs and steep in the cane spirit for 7 or 8 days. Strain and use as a scalp massage for toning hair or combating excessive oiliness and dandruff. For best results massage well twice weekly.

HAIR CARE

This is a favourite treatment for preserving hair and thickening, strengthening and conditioning it.

250 ml (1 cup) rosemary flowers and tips of stems
1¼ litres (5 cups) white wine
160 ml (²/₃ cup) honey
160 ml (²/₃ cup) sweet almond oil

Pour the wine over the rosemary and stand overnight. Strain rosemary the next morning. Combine oil and honey and add to the strained rosemary. Shake well and store.

Pour 25–37,5 ml (2–3 tbls) into a cup, stand the cup in hot water to warm it, and then rub the lotion into the hair, massaging well and combing through. Wrap head in a warm towel and leave on for half an hour at least before washing hair with your usual shampoo.

If this is done once a week you will begin to notice a wonderful improvement in the condition of your hair.

A HAIR RUB FOR BALDNESS AND HAIR CONDITIONING

25 ml (2 tbls) almond oil
10 ml (2 tsp) rosemary oil

Mix the oils in a cup and stand the cup in a pan of boiling water. Stir well, testing that it does not become too hot.

Massage warmed oil well into the scalp and then wrap a hot towel around the head for at least 30 minutes. Shampoo normally, preferably using a rosemary shampoo.

HEADACHE

LAVENDER HEADACHE CURE

440 ml (1¾ cups) lavender flowers
310 ml (1¼ cups) apple cider vinegar
310 ml (1¼ cups) rose-water

Rose-water is made by boiling red fragrant rose petals in water. Place petals in a pot with enough water to cover them. Bring to the boil, then cool and strain. Keep the rose-water in the refrigerator.

Place lavender flowers in a screw-top jar. Cover with the vinegar and leave for a week in a cool dark place. Shake well daily. After one week, strain the liquid through muslin and discard the lavender flowers. Add the rose-water and bottle.

For relieving a bad headache saturate a wad or two of cotton wool and place on the temples or forehead or over the eyes. To combat fatigue use the same lotion as a toilet water on tired feet and on wrists.

NAUSEA

For relief of nausea sip hot water with a squeeze of lemon juice.

SKIN

ECZEMA WASH

250 ml (1 cup) ajuga roots
3 litres (12 cups) water
250 ml (1 cup) elder flowers (Sambucus nigra)
250 ml (1 cup) elder leaves, well packed

Boil ingredients together in the water and stand overnight. Strain, bottle and keep in the refrigerator. Use as a wash or dab onto the affected area twice or three times daily.

PRICKLY HEAT CURE

Cotton wool pads, liberally soaked in vinegar, should be applied to the itchy areas; this is particularly effective in elbow joints, behind knees and in the groin (the smell soon evaporates).

ELDER FLOWER SUNBURN CREAM

100 g (½ cup) white shortening or plain aqueous cream
250 ml (1 cup) elder flowers, removed from stalks

Simmer ingredients gently, stirring constantly, for 15 minutes. Strain into warm jars and cork when cool.

Use on minor burns, sunburn and heat rash.

WATERCRESS COMPLEXION CURE

Eating a lot of watercress and drinking water will improve the complexion. Alternatively, wash the face with a cooled brew of 500 ml (2 cups) watercress leaves that have been steeped in 250 ml (1 cup) boiling water.

Watercress, eaten daily, will also help bleeding gums.

FRECKLE BLEACH

75 ml (6 tbls) buttermilk
5 ml (1 tsp) grated fresh horseradish
almond oil

Lightly oil the skin with almond oil. Mix buttermilk and horseradish well and apply. Leave on for 20 minutes and then wash off with warm water.

DANDELION FRECKLE BLEACH

250 ml (1 cup) freshly opened dandelion flowers
940 ml (3¾ cups) water

Boil up together and simmer for 30 minutes, then strain through a sieve lined with muslin. Wash the face in this lotion night and morning and freckles will fade.

Keep in the refrigerator if making a large quantity.

CREAM FOR CHAPPED HANDS

4 slices lemon
250 ml (1 cup) milk

Leave the lemon in the milk for about 4 hours until thickened. Use to soothe rough skin on hands, knees and elbows.

Keep excess in the refrigerator.

ACNE

Eat an orange daily to clear teenage acne. Washing the face in water with the juice of a lemon squeezed into it is also effective.

Drink freshly squeezed lemon juice in a glass of tap water first thing in the morning.

SORE THROAT

SORE THROAT AND COUGH GARGLE

250 ml (1 cup) elder blossoms

250 ml (1 cup) sage leaves
6 cloves
750 ml (3 cups) water

Boil ingredients in water for 10 minutes and then stand and steep. Strain and add 5 ml sweet almond oil. Shake well and gargle frequently with this brew.

SORE THROAT GARGLE

125 ml (½ cup) cider vinegar
5 ml (1 tsp) salt
250 ml (1 cup) hot water

Mix well and gargle frequently. Do not swallow.

*See also *Fever Vinegar* under FEVERS

SPRAINS AND SWELLINGS

GREEN ELDER SPRAIN OINTMENT

750 ml (3 cups) fresh elder leaves, well pressed into the measure
200 g (1 cup) white shortening or plain aqueous cream
few drops oil of lavender

Heat ingredients together gently for 15 minutes, stirring well. Strain through a sieve, discard leaves and pour liquid into shallow bottles or tins. Allow to cool before corking.

Use on bruises, sprains or chilblains, covering with a gauze bandage overnight.

FIG AND POTATO POULTICE

This is a comfortable poultice for swellings and painful joints.

10 ml (2 tsp) dried figs, chopped and soaked in hot water for one hour or
250 ml (1 cup) fresh figs, chopped
1 medium potato, grated
10 ml (2 tsp) glycerine

Mix all ingredients into a paste. Spread on a folded bandage so that the mixture does not touch the skin directly. Bind in place and leave overnight. Renew in the morning.

*See also *Potato Poultice* under BOILS

STINGS

WASP AND BEE STINGS

Immediately apply a pad of cotton wool soaked in vinegar.

STOMACH

STOMACH ACHE REMEDY

125 ml (½ cup) fresh mint
125 ml (½ cup) chopped endive

Steep in 500 ml (2 cups) white wine for 24 hours. Add 5 ml (1 tsp) thyme and 2 ml (½ tsp) dill seeds and stand for another 24 hours. Strain and take 125 ml (½ cup) before meals.

STOMACH ACHE TEA

250 ml (1 cup) boiling water
4 thumb-length pieces peppermint

Pour boiling water over peppermint, allow to draw for 2–3 minutes, then sip while still hot.

DIARRHOEA REMEDY

200 g (1 cup) brown rice
1,5 litres (6 cups) water
25 ml (2 tbls) honey

Boil the rice in the water for half an hour. Strain and sweeten the rice water with honey. Add the juice of a lemon if desired, and drink freely.

COLIC OR GRIPE WATER

125 ml (½ cup) caraway seeds
750 ml (3 cups) hot water

Bruise the seeds by rolling them with a rolling pin and infuse in the hot water overnight. Strain through muslin. Take 5–20 ml (1–4 tsp) daily at intervals to relieve colic in infants, and 10 ml (1 dessertsp) 3 times daily for older children. Keep the brew in the refrigerator between times and warm a little for each dose.

POTATO REMEDY FOR HEARTBURN, STOMACH ULCERS AND INDIGESTION

Eat a walnut-sized piece of raw potato before meals. This neutralizes the acidity in the stomach before the food reaches it and aids the digestion. Be sure to choose a piece of potato that has no eyes on it as these are poisonous.

TEETH

TOOTHACHE CURES

A wad of cotton wool soaked in oil of cloves and placed on the aching tooth will greatly relieve the pain.

Heat 12,5 ml (1 tbls) honey and add 5 cloves. Stir well, stand for 15 minutes, then chew the cloves with the aching tooth, slowly and gently, to release the soothing clove oil.

STRAWBERRY TEETH WHITENER

Rub a fresh strawberry over discoloured teeth and leave on for 5 minutes. Rinse off with warm water to which a pinch of bicarbonate of soda has been added and dissolved.

The ground cover strawberry with its brilliant red berries is equally effective for removing stains from the teeth.

*For bleeding gums eat watercress daily.
*See also *Earache Bag* under EARACHE

WARTS

WART REMOVER

Apply the milky juice of a fig leaf or a dandelion plant to the wart. Alternatively, cut a piece of banana skin and apply the inside to the wart, holding it in place with a strip of plaster. Apply a fresh piece of skin daily for ten days.

WHITLOWS

WHITLOWS OR INFECTIONS OF THE NAILS

Heat a whole lemon in hot water. Make a tunnel down the centre of the lemon and pack it with salt and fresh pine-needles. Bury the affected finger in this tunnel and keep it there as long as possible. Repeat whenever necessary.

WOUNDS AND SORES

CARROT POULTICE FOR SORES

Grate 2 medium-sized carrots and apply the pulp to the wound or swelling. Bind in place with a clean bandage and renew twice daily.

As a general guide to nature's 'surgical dressings' the following plants all have healing properties. They can be used with safety and results will be swift. For grazes, cuts, deep wounds and even old sores use the tender leaves of:

cabbage
lettuce
violet
grapevine
castor-oil
morning glory

water-lily
chickweed
yarrow
the inner leaves of the mealie cob
arum lily
periwinkle
honeysuckle
onion
mulberry
horseradish
comfrey
carrot
hypericum

When using any of the above herbs bind in place with a crêpe bandage and replace leaves with fresh ones morning and evening. Repeat until the wound stops suppurating and heals healthily.

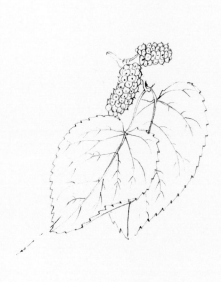

13
ASTROLOGY AND HERBS

If we are to consider how far back herbalism began and how far back astrology began we shall see that they in fact travelled hand in hand through a celestial zodiac, the great wide circular path along which the planets travel. The planets in turn link to the body and, in the ancient Doctrine of Signatures, plants link to the body too, thus forming a great fascinating 'oneness' with nature.

The practice of astrology is believed to have originated in ancient Babylonia where the priests, having noted the five visible planets besides the sun and moon, related the movements of the planets to the major events in their lives. The nature of these events then enabled these ancient astronomers to accredit the planets with certain general characteristics. They then divided the zodiac into twelve equal parts, each corresponding to a constellation along the ecliptic and each endowed with its own characteristics. Thus were the new ideas born, proved and carried along the trade routes to India, from whence they spread rapidly throughout the East.

Between 700 and 200 BC this accumulation of astronomical data gathered by the Babylonian priesthood was gradually added to. The first horoscopes were cast by learned Jews and Egyptians who adapted the starry wisdom to their own needs. However, it was really the Greeks who turned astrology into the logical and unified system with which we are familiar today. Although astrology was known to them from ancient times, it was the invasion of Mesopotamia and the resulting contact with Babylon that stimulated fresh interest and study. The knowledge subsequently gained was assimilated by the major philosophical schools, as was recognition of the influence of the stars on human affairs.

Our solar system is part of a gigantic cosmic pattern, so enormous it is difficult for the layman to comprehend. The characteristics of this pattern are discernible from the position of the planets at any given moment. This means that anything happening anywhere in the cosmic pattern will to some extent affect the pattern and this is how astrologers can codify the connections known as 'astrological correspondences' with the things of the universe, ie connections between plants, colours, scents, precious stones, minerals and qualities – and these correspondences in turn are of value in the understanding of nature.

Herbs, like everything else, conform with the pattern of nature and every plant is related to one of the signs of the zodiac and comes under the influence of a particular planet. In just the same way parts of the body, and specific organs of the body, fall under this influence of the planets. Their zodiacal position must always be taken into account and those parts of the body governed by the sign in which they are placed will be affected.

185

It is impossible in this short treatise to discuss all aspects of herbal or medical astrology, since this is a wide and extensive field. The purpose in this brief outline, therefore, is to give the man in the street a general idea regarding the herbs most likely to prove beneficial to certain ailments. Only an intensive study of herbal astrology would enable one to become familiar with the combination of the planets and the herbs under them and in so doing derive some benefit by using the knowledge to effect relief from a particular affliction.

Two hundred and fifty years ago a doctor of medicine in Europe was obliged to pass an astrological examination and, if found deficient in the knowledge of astrology, was denied a licence to practise his profession! Equally amazing is the fact that the eminent Greek scholar Pythagoras (569–470 BC) contributed greatly to astrological learning by founding a college in the south of Italy where herbalism, astrology, numerology and healing by colour and sound were taught – particularly interesting as we in the latter part of the twentieth century now consider these 'old' things to be 'new' age development.

The Doctrine of Signatures is another ancient explanation of herbalism and maintains a similar belief in the essential oneness of nature, a belief which is also common to astrology. As far as the herbalist is concerned this means that the healing virtues of various plants can be discerned from their appearance or their position, in other words the particular 'signature' that they bear. For example, many yellow-flowered plants help jaundice or urinary infections, while heart's ease, the tiny wild pansy with heart-shaped leaves, aids heart conditions. A plant growing in a marshy, damp place will help rheumatism, which is generally aggravated by damp. One such plant is the willow, once an important standby in the treatment of rheumatic fever; the same willow contains a substance called acetysalicylic acid, which played a part in the development of aspirin, undoubtedly one of the most efficient pain killers ever discovered.

Paracelsus, a medical doctor born in 1493, believed strongly in this Doctrine of Signatures, as did Giambattista della Porta (1543–1615), a scientist, magician and alchemist. The latter's fascination with herbs and devotion to the Doctrine of Signatures gave us our basic knowledge and it was he who first voiced the idea that plants common to a particular region would cure the afflictions of the inhabitants, the theory being that the local climate was responsible for the disease and its cure would therefore be found locally as well, an important concept which is coming more and more into evidence today. We in South Africa thus need increasingly to turn to our own plant kingdom, more particularly to our indigenous plants, for the healing we need; we should not import overseas medicines and cures for their climates and conditions differ totally from ours.

A thirteenth century Italian mathematician, Fabonacci, drew attention to the sacred geometry in the plants of healing and nourishment, and the natural phenomena of the arrangement of leaves and petals, which became known as the 'Fabonacci series'. Branching, which is a major functional pattern of natural growth, is controlled by the Fabonacci series and, because of its appearance in the pentagon, the golden central section can be found in all flowers having five petals or multiples of five, eg the daisy family, the rose family and all the flowers of edible fruit-bearing plants (cucurbits, apples, apricots). Thus five signals to man his medicines and his foods and so many herb flowers have that sacred five-petalled signature – five symbolising the flowering or quintessence of life.

186

Traditional medicine considered seven-petalled plants to be poisonous, and among these are the Belladonna or nightshade family. Exotic flowers like the orchid, the azalea and the passion flower are all governed by pentagonal symmetry and the pentagon is the symbol of life, particularly human life, and plants are the basis for human life.

There is much discrepancy in literature regarding exactly which plants belong to which sign, and also the way in which one goes about treating disease astrologically. After researching many astrological sources, I have managed to condense some of the information and have compiled a chart of the common and most well-known plants. This chart is meant only to interest the reader and to show that even today those plants are still being used, their results speaking for themselves.

For further reading:

Conway, David. *The Magic of Herbs*. London: Jonathan Cape, 1973.

Hall, Manly P. *The Secret Teachings of All Ages*. Los Angeles: Philosophical Research Society Inc., 1977.

House, Harry C. and Audrey M. *The Practical Herbalist and Herbal Astrology*. Seattle: Harry C. House, 1961.

Sign	Dates	Ruling planet	Part of body governed	Number	Metal
Aries The Ram cardinal, fire	21 March – 19 April	Mars	head, eyes, face, upper jaw, right and left carotid arteries	13	iron, steel, sulphur
Taurus The Bull fixed, earth	20 April – 20 May	Venus	neck, throat, ears, palate, tonsils, cerebellum, occipital region, 7 cervical vertebrae, larynx, vocal chords, pharynx, lower jaw	14	copper
Gemini The Twins mutable, air	21 May – 21 June	Mercury	shoulders, clavicle, scapula, arms, hands, upper ribs, breath, oxygenation of blood, bronchii, lungs	17	quicksilver
Cancer The Crab cardinal, water	22 June – 22 July	Moon	stomach, breasts, digestion, lower part of the lungs, oesophagus, diaphragm, liver, stomach	18	silver, aluminium antimony
Leo The Lion fixed, fire	23 July – 22 August	Sun	spine, back, heart, circulation	19	gold
Virgo The Virgin mutable, earth	23 August – 22 September	Mercury	abdominal and umbilical region, liver, spleen, duodenum, intestines	2	quicksilver

tter	Tone	Note	Colour	Gem	Some propitious plants
	High C	Do	light magenta, claret, reds, maroon	amethyst, flint, bloodstone, ochre, diamond, jasper, garnet	pine, hemp, mustard, broom, poppy, peppers, holly, marjoram, dock, thistle, fever, basil, tarragon, sorrel, rosemary, horseradish, parsley, garlic, onions, nettles, radishes
	Low E	La	dark yellows, pale blue, pastels	moss agate, emerald, alabaster, white coral, white opaque stones, carnelian	daisy, myrtle, mint, elder, flax, lily, spinach, moss, feverfew, yarrow, dandelion, gourds, thyme, catmint, larkspur, lovage, pennyroyal, tansy
P,	High B	Mi	lighter shades of violet, checks, blue-grey, mauves	beryl crystal, aquamarine, agate, striped stones	carrot, pomegranate, tansy, yarrow, lavender, penngreek, dill, marjoram, parsley, privet, southernwood, fennel, caraway, horehound
, Ts,	High F	Ti	light greens, silver, white, opalescent and iridescent hues, silvery grey	emerald, black onyx, pearls, selenite, chalk, white stones	onions, chickweed, daisy, water plants, lemon balm, rushes, hyssop, squash, honeysuckle, jasmine, camphor, cucumber, melons, waterlily, wallflower, lettuce
	High D	Re	light orange, golden shades, deep yellows, orange-reds	ruby, sardonyx, diamond, soft yellow stones	St Johns wort, angelica, chamomile, fennel, rosemary, salad burnet, peony, dill, daffodil, bay laurel, borage, mistletoe, marigold, rue, mint, almond, lavender, parsley, olive
	Low B	Mi	dark violet, checks and tartans, slate grey	jasper, hyacinth, flints	barley, oats, rye, wheat, lavender, valerian, millet, endive, privet, southernwood, savory, fennel, dill, parsley, marjoram, azaleas, caraway, celery, ferns, germander, mulberry

Sign	Dates	Ruling planet	Part of body governed	Number	Metal
Libra The Scales cardinal, air	23 September – 23 October	Venus	lumbar spine, kidneys, reproductive fluids, skin, adrenals, internal generative organs	3	copper
Scorpio The Scorpion fixed, water	24 October – 21 November	Mars Pluto	nose, pelvis, kidneys, uterus, sacral vertebrae, bladder, red corpuscles, uterus, genitals, rectum, prostate, external reproductive organs	4	iron, steel sulphur
Sagittarius The Archer mutable, fire	22 November – 21 December	Jupiter	hips, femur, ilium, coccygeal vertebrae, thighs, sciatic nerve, bladder	7	tin
Capricorn The Goat cardinal, earth	22 December – 19 January	Saturn	knees, skin, hair, joints of the body, arterial system, nerves, teeth	8	lead
Aquarius The Water Carrier fixed, air	20 January – 18 February	Saturn Uranus	legs below the knees, ankles, cartilage, ligaments, blood and circulation	9	lead
Pisces The Fishes mutable, water	19 February – 20 March	Neptune Jupiter Uranus	feet, toes, bones of the middle ear, lymphatic system	12	tin

tter	Tone	Note	Colour	Gem	Some propitious plants
	High E	La	light yellows, pastel colours, light blue, light gold	opal, diamond, jade, beryl	white rose, strawberry, violet, foxglove, watercress, primrose, pansy, soapwort, heart's ease, lemon thyme, yarrow, sorrel, pennyroyal, mint, elder, tansy, fennel, valerian, columbine, peppermint, catnip, ajuga, golden rod
	Low C	Do	deeper shades of red, wine, maroon, deep yellow	topaz, malachite, jasper, bloodstone	basil, heather, horehound, bramble, bean, leek, wormwood, garlic, mustard, nettle, tarragon, catmint, horseradish, hyssop, rhubarb
	High A	So	blues, mauves, navy blue, dark indigo, red	red garnet, turquoise, carbuncle	feverfew, mallow, lemon balm, chervil, hyssop, onion, beetroot, borage, dandelion, sage, apricots, asparagus, endive, figs, red roses, tansy, sugar cane
Ch	Low G	Fa	dark blues, purple, brown, black, sage green, grey, indigo	onyx, jet, moonstone, lapislazuli, sardonyx, coal	comfrey, black poppy, nightshade, pansy, wintergreen, mullein, beetroot, woad, horsetail, amaranthus, shepherd's purse, plantain, heart's ease, opium, marijuana
	High G	Fa	sky blue, light blue	opal, blue sapphire, black pearl	plantain, quince, barley, willow, marijuana, spinach, parsnip, tobacco, comfrey, elder, thistle, frankincense, myrrh, holly, ivy
	Low A	So	sea green, deep blues, dark purple	peridot, sand, moonstone, pumice, coral	water mosses, ferns, seaweed, asparagus, watercress, sage, mint, gillyflower, mulberry, almond, chestnuts, olives

191

14
THE LANGUAGE OF FLOWERS

In days long ago and far away flowers had a language all of their own. A whole letter could be written in a tussie-mussie or a posy.

The word 'posy' dates back to the sixteenth century and a tussie-mussie is a posy in which each sprig of rosemary, honeysuckle or lavender conveyed a thought or message, an important means of communication, especially for young lovers. There could have been some confusion, however, for the meanings of certain plants differed from county to county and the unspoken word in a bouquet had to be carefully deciphered.

After a survey of several sources the language of flowers below is as safe as it can be recorded for these are the meanings used most often.

Flower	*Meaning*
Acacia	friendship
Acanthus (bear's breeches)	artifice
Almond	hope
Aloe	grief
Alyssum	worth beyond beauty
Amaranthus	affectation
Amaryllis	pride, timidity
Anemone	forsaken
Apple	temptation
Arum lily	forsaken
Aster	variety
Azalea	temperance
Basil	hatred
Bay	glory
Bindweed	humility
Borage	courage
Box	stoicism
Bramble	loneliness, remorse
Broom	humility
Bulrush	indiscretion
Buttercup	ingratitude
Cabbage	profit
Cactus	warmth
Calycanthus	benevolence

Camellia (red)	unpretending excellence
Camellia (white)	perfected loveliness
Candytuft	indifference
Carnation (red)	my poor heart
Carnation (white)	refusal
Carnation (yellow)	disdain
Cedar	strength
Chamomile	energy in adversity
Cherry (flowering)	deception
Chervil	sincerity
Chickweed	rendezvous
Chicory	frugality
Chrysanthemum	cheerful under adversity
Chrysanthemum (white)	truth
Cinquefoil	material affection
Clematis	mental beauty
Clove	dignity
Clover (red)	industry
Clover (white)	think of me
Columbine	folly
Convolvulus (morning glory)	repose
Convolvulus (perennial)	extinguished hopes
Coreopsis	always cheerful
Coriander	hidden worth
Corn	riches
Cress	stability, power
Crocus	abuse not
Cyclamen	diffidence
Cypress	mourning, death
Daffodil	regard
Dahlia	instability
Daisy	innocence
Daisy (wild)	I will think on this
Dandelion	rustic oracle
Day lily	coquetry
Dead leaves	sadness
Dock	patience
Elder	zealousness
Endive	frugality
Eupatorium	delay
Everlasting	never-ceasing remembrance
Fennel	worthy of praise
Fern	fascination
Fig	argument
Fir	time
Flax	domestic industry
Forget-me-not	true love
Foxglove	insincerity

Fuchsia	taste
Garland of roses	reward of virtue
Geranium	melancholy
Geranium (ivy leaf)	bridal favour
Geranium (lemon-scented)	unexpected meeting
Geranium (nutmeg)	expected meeting
Geranium (rose-scented)	preference
Geranium (scarlet)	comforting
Germander	facility
Golden rod	precaution
Gooseberry	anticipation
Gourd	extent
Grass	submission
Guelder-rose	winter, age
Harebell	grief
Hawthorn	hope
Heather	solitude
Heliotrope	devotion
Hibiscus	delicate beauty
Holly	foresight
Hollyhock	ambition
Honesty	honesty, fascination
Honeysuckle	generous and devoted affection
Hoya	sculpture
Hyacinth	sport, a game
Hydrangea	heartlessness
Hyssop	cleanliness
Iris	message
Ivy	fidelity, marriage
Jasmine	amiability
Jasmine (starflower cluster)	separation
Jasmine (yellow)	grace and elegance
Jonquil	I desire a return of affection
Juniper	succour
Lantana	rigour
Larkspur	lightness
Laurel	glory
Laurestine	a token
Lavender	distrust
Lemon	zest
Lemon balm (melissa)	sympathy
Lemon flowers	fidelity in love
Lettuce	cold-hearted
Lichen	dejection
Licorice	I declare against
Lily (yellow)	gaiety, falsehood
Lily-of-the-Valley	return of happiness
Lime tree	conjugal love

Lobelia	malevolence
London pride	frivolity
Lotus	eloquence
Love-in-a-mist	perplexity
Love-lies-bleeding	hopeless
Lucerne	life
Lupine	imagination
Madonna lily	purity
Magnolia	love of nature
Mallow	mildness
Maple	reserve
Marigold	grief
Marigold (*Tagetes* family)	vulgarity
Marjoram	blushes
Mesembryanthemum	idleness
Michaelmas daisy	farewell
Mignonette	your qualities surpass your charms
Mint	virtue
Mistletoe	I surmount difficulties
Mock orange	counterfeit
Morning glory	repose
Morning glory (perennial)	extinguished hopes
Moss	maternal love
Mulberry tree	I shall not survive you
Mushroom	suspicion
Mustard	indifference
Myrtle	love
Narcissus	egotism
Nasturtium	patriotism
Nettle	slander
Night-blooming cerens	transient beauty
Night convolvulus	night
Oak	hospitality
Oats	music
Oleander	beware
Olive	peace
Orange blossom	your purity equals your loveliness
Orange flowers	chastity
Orange leaves	bridal festivity
Orange tree	generosity
Ox-eye daisy	patience
Palm	victory
Pansy	thoughts
Parsley	festivity
Passion flower (granadilla)	religious superstition
Pea	happy marriage, many children
Peach	your qualities are uneqalled
Peach blossom	I am your captive

Pear	affection
Pear tree	comfort
Pennyroyal	flee away
Peony	shame
Peppermint	warmth of feeling
Periwinkle	friendship
Phlox	unanimity
Pineapple	warmth, hospitality, you are perfect
Pine (spruce)	hope in adversity
Pine tree	pity
Pink (carnation)	woman's love
Pink (dianthus)	pure love
Pink (dianthus, variegated)	refusal
Pink (gillyflower)	bonds of affection
Plane tree	genius
Plum tree	fidelity
Pomegranate	foolishness
Pomegranate flower	mature elegance
Poplar	courage
Poppy (red)	consolation
Poppy (scarlet, field)	fantastic extravagance
Potato	benevolence
Prickly pear	satire
Primrose	early youth
Primrose (evening anothera)	inconstancy
Privet	prohibition
Quaking grass	agitation
Quince	temptation
Ranunculus	you are radiant
Rock rose (cistus)	popular flavour
Rose (red)	love, true love
Rose (red and white together)	unity
Rose (yellow)	jealous love
Rose (cabbage)	ambassador of love
Rose (dogrose)	pleasure and pain
Rose (musk)	capricious beauty
Rosemary	remembrance
Rudbeckia	justice
Rue	disdain
Rush	docility
Sage	domestic virtue
St John's wort	animosity
Scabious	unfortunate love
Snapdragon	presumption
Snowdrop	hope
Sorrel	affection
Southernwood	jest
Spearmint	warmth

196

Speedwell	female fidelity
Stock	lasting beauty
Stonecrop	tranquillity
Strawberry	esteem, love
Sunflower	haughtiness
Sweet basil	good wishes
Sweetpea	departure, delicate pleasure
Sycamore	curiosity
Syringa	memory
Tamarisk	crime
Tansy	I declare war against you
Tendrils of climbing plants	ties
Thistle	retaliation
Thorn-apple	deceit
Thorns (branch of)	severity
Thrift	sympathy
Thyme	activity
Traveller's joy	safety
Tuberose	dangerous pleasures
Tulip	fame
Tulip (red)	declaration of love
Tulip (yellow)	hopeless love
Turnip	charity
Valerian	accommodating
Veronica	fidelity
Vine	intoxication
Violet	faithfulness
Wallflower	fidelity in adversity
Walnut	intellect
Waterlily	purity of heart
Watermelon	friendship of sharing
Wheat stalk	riches
Willow	freedom
Willow (weeping)	mourning
Wormwood	absence
Xeranthemum	cheerfulness under adversity
Yarrow	war

197

HERB AND AILMENT CHART

... and God created medicines out of the earth, he that is wise will not abhor them ....

ABSCESS: bergamot, periwinkle (vinca major), castor oil, pumpkin, rue.

ACHES AND PAINS: bergamot, castor oil, eucomis, mints, mustard, myrtle, wilde als.

ACNE: rhubarb, nasturtium, elder, comfrey, salad burnet.

ANAEMIA: amaranthus, chicory, elder, grape, nettle, pumpkin, watercress.

ANTIBIOTIC: garlic, grape, hypericum, nasturtium, radish, thyme.

ANTISEPTIC: bay, chamomile, columbine, garlic, lavender, myrtle, southernwood, thyme, wormwood.

ARTHRITIS: celery, comfrey, feverfew, garlic, honeysuckle, hypericum, mustard, nettle, parsley, vinca rosea.

ASTHMA: comfrey, ginger, honeysuckle, mignonette.

ASTRINGENT: amaranthus, columbine, mint, myrtle, salad burnet.

BEDWETTING: catnip, marjoram, verbascum (mullein).

BLADDER AILMENTS: borage, asparagus, celery, hydrangea, Job's tears, parsley.

BLEEDING: nettle, yarrow.

BLOOD CLEANSER: chicory, chives, crab apple, grape, mustard, nettle, parsley, pumpkin, radish.

BLOOD POISONING: crab apple, nettle.

BLOOD PRESSURE: celery, chives, garlic, tansy.

BOILS: arum, nasturtium, castor oil, pumpkin, rue.

BRONCHITIS: bergamot, comfrey, elder, garlic, honeysuckle, Job's tears, rue, maidenhair fern, pennyroyal, verbascum (mullein).

BRUISES: bay, borage, castor oil, comfrey, iris, myrtle, tansy, wormwood.

198

BURNS:	acanthus, agave, aloe, arum, comfrey, elder, sour fig.
CALLOUSES:	ivy.
CALMING:	lemon balm (melissa), borage, catnip, chamomile, columbine, elder, granadilla, rock rose, rose, thyme.
CANCER:	skin cancer – elder, grape, parsley as a preventative.
CHEST AILMENTS:	comfrey, asparagus, elder, horehound, verbascum (mullein).
CHILLS:	lemon balm (melissa), ginger, thyme.
CIRCULATION:	calendula.
COLDS:	thyme, wilde als, lemon balm (melissa), bergamot, buttercup, chamomile, elder, ginger, horehound, lucerne, mustard, sage, winter savory.
COLIC:	angelica, bergamot, catnip, chamomile, lemon verbena, mustard quince, radish, rhubarb, wilde als.
CONSTIPATION:	agave, aloe, castor oil, chamomile, iris, quince, rhubarb, violet, water lily, wormwood.
CONVULSIONS:	catnip, chamomile.
CORNS:	ivy.
COUGH:	lemon balm (melissa), buttercup, chamomile, elder, honeysuckle, horehound, lovage, maidenhair fern, watercress, mustard, thyme.
	whooping cough: prickly pear, violet, wilde als.
CRAMP:	chamomile, ginger, rosemary.
CUTS:	periwinkle (vinca major), rosemary, salad burnet, yarrow.
CYSTITIS:	asparagus, celery, borage.
DEODORANT:	parsley, sage.
DIABETES:	nettle, prickly pear, vinca rosea.
DIARRHOEA:	amaranthus, geranium (scented), ginger, periwinkle (vinca major), quince, yarrow, sour fig, water lily, wormwood.
DIURETIC:	asparagus, celery, fennel, nettle, strawberry, yarrow.
DIZZINESS:	rosemary, mint, lemon balm (melissa).
DYSENTERY:	geranium (scented), ginger, hypericum, Job's tears, quince, sour fig, wormwood, yarrow.

EARACHE:	foxglove, ivy pig's ear cotyledon, tansy, verbascum (mullein), wormwood.
ECZEMA:	ajuga, calendula, grape, nettle, salad burnet, soapwort, strawberry.
EYE AILMENTS:	borage, calendula, chamomile, strawberry, chicory, cornflower, elder, foxglove, tansy, watercress, golden rod, grape, ivy, mignonette, nasturtium.
FAINTING:	rosemary.
FEVER:	borage, garlic, catnip, grape, strawberry, tansy, yarrow.
FLATULENCE:	angelica, anise, asparagus, bergamot, catnip, caraway, eucomis, lemon verbena, mustard, tarragon.
FRACTURES:	comfrey.
GARGLE:	amaranthus, sweet basil, chamomile, quince, mints, rock rose, sour fig.
GLANDS:	buttercup, hydrangea, ivy.
GOUT:	germander.
GRAZES:	rosemary, salad burnet, water lily, yarrow.
HAEMORRAGE:	nettle, yarrow.
HAEMORRHOIDS:	myrtle, comfrey, yarrow.
HAIR TONIC:	sweet basil, bergamot, castor oil, chamomile, maidenhair fern, nettle, quince, rosemary, soapwort.
HAYFEVER:	mints, pennyroyal.
HEADACHE:	feverfew, foxglove, ivy, lavender, rosemary, violet.
HEART CONDITIONS:	foxglove, yarrow, rosemary, rue, tansy.
HEARTBURN:	anise, fennel, caraway.
INDIGESTION:	sour fig, nasturtium, oreganum, radish, hyssop, lemon verbena, lovage, angelica, anise, bay, catnip, caraway, chamomile, chicory, coriander; crab apple, dill, fennel, ginger, golden rod, granadilla.
INFLAMMATION:	comfrey, hollyhock, mustard, sour fig, water lily.
INFLUENZA:	comfrey, mustard, rue, winter savory, wilde als.
INSECT BITES:	borage, comfrey, cornflower, mint, vinca rosea.
INSECT REPELLENT:	rosemary, rue, santolina, sweet basil, caraway, tansy, southernwood, elder, feverfew, germander, marigold, wormwood, mint, pennyroyal, prickly pear, pyrethrum.

200

INSOMNIA:	chamomile, lemon balm (melissa), catnip, columbine, elder, ginger, lavender, rose.
ITCHING:	elder, mints.
JAUNDICE:	asparagus, chicory, golden rod, ivy, parsley, rosemary, wormwood
KIDNEY AILMENTS:	asparagus, borage, tansy, celery, ginger, golden rod, hydrangea, Job's tears, lucerne, nettle, parsley.
LUNG INFECTIONS:	asparagus, comfrey, garlic, mustard, rue, verbascum (mullein), wilde als.
MENSTRUATION:	catnip, columbine, yarrow, strawberry, feverfew, ginger, hollyhock, myrtle, nettle, periwinkle (vinca major).
MISCARRIAGE:	hollyhock, strawberry, wormwood.
MUMPS:	buttercup, ivy.
NAUSEA:	bergamot, ginger, mints, rose.
NERVES:	lemon balm (melissa), catnip, columbine, lavender, mignonette, nasturtium, rose.
NEURALGIA:	celery, mignonette, sage.
NOSE PROBLEMS:	*bleeding:* yarrow, periwinkle (vinca major). *blocked:* bergamot, water lily, pennyroyal.
OBESITY:	fennel, celery, asparagus, garlic, parsley, wormwood.
PAIN:	catnip, eucomis, mustard.
PNEUMONIA:	comfrey, garlic, golden rod, wilde als, maidenhair fern, mustard, yarrow, pennyroyal, rue, verbascum (mullein).
POST OPERATIVE:	comfrey, grape, sage.
PURGATIVE:	agave, aloe, castor oil, chamomile, nettle rhubarb.
RASH:	ajuga, aloe, elder, cornflower, honeysuckle, water lily.
RELAXANT:	lemon balm (melissa), catnip, elder, feverfew, lavender, marjoram.
RHEUMATISM:	agave, asparagus, celery, comfrey, garlic, honeysuckle, hypercum, nettle, vinca rosea, yarrow.
SCIATICA:	garlic, hydrangea, hypericum, mustard, nettle.
SEDATIVE:	lemon balm (melissa), borage, catnip, columbine, elder, foxglove, ginger, grenadilla, marjoram, mignonette.
SINUS:	mints, pennyroyal.

SKIN DISORDERS:	ajuga, calendula, elder, marjoram, mint, myrtle, salad burnet, watercress.
SLIMMING:	celery, fennel, asparagus, garlic, parsley.
SORE THROAT:	wilde als, yarrow, bergamot, buttercup, sage, sour fig, elder, ginger, honeysuckle, water lily, marjoram, nasturtium, rock rose.
SORES:	aloe, arum, calendula, castor oil, prickly pear, hypericum, nasturtium, periwinkle (vinca major), water lily.
SPRAINS:	comfrey, mustard.
STIMULANT:	chamomile, celery, mint, nasturtium.
STINGS:	comfrey, cornflower, mint.
STOMACH DISORDERS:	chamomile, crab apple, iris, lovage, mint, nasturtium, strawberry.
STRESS:	lucerne, mignonette, lemon balm (melissa), comfrey.
STYES:	strawberry, tansy.
SUNBURN:	ajuga, mint, salad burnet, water lily.
SWELLING:	borage, comfrey, foxglove.
TONIC:	rosemary, strawberry, garden valerian, amaranthus, asparagus, calendula, catnip, chamomile, chervil, chicory, chives, garlic, golden rod, grape, lucerne, radish.
TOOTHACHE:	castor oil, tarragon.
TUMOUR:	castor oil, foxglove, grape.
ULCERS:	aloe, amaranthus, chamomile, columbine, comfrey, cornflower, periwinkle (vinca major).
VAGINAL DOUCHE:	amaranthus, chamomile, feverfew, rock rose, water lily.
VARICOSE VEINS:	tansy.
VOMITING:	mint.
WARTS:	castor oil, pig's ear cotyledon, vinca rosea.
WORMS:	sweet basil, castor oil, garlic, hollyhock, nasturtium, pumpkin seeds, wormwood.
WOUNDS:	bergamot, calendula, castor oil, comfrey, cornflower, golden rod, grape, hollyhock, hypericum, nasturtium, periwinkle (vinca major), pig's ear cotyledon.

EPILOGUE

I've weighed all that has been written or said about the subject and borrowed from other authors that I found agreeable to reason and experience; taking care to fetch in and bundle up what I found straggling in their bulky writings and not easy to come at.

Not that this performance is only a collection, though I should not be troubled if the world thought it so, since it is not vainglory but the encouragement of Herbalists that I have in view. He who considers it narrowly will find that collection was not my only task and that I have pointed to such things as are not to be met elsewhere.

from *The Dutch Gardener*
Henry van Oelsen
1703

BIBLIOGRAPHY

Bairacli-Levy, J de. *The Illustrated Herbal Handbook*. London: Faber and Faber, 1974.

Graf, Alfred. *Exotica*. USA: Roehrs Co.

Hauschka, Rudolf. *The Nature of Substance*. London: Vincent Stuart, 1966.

House, Harry C and Audrey M. *The Practical Herbalist*.

Stuart, Malcolm. *The Encyclopaedia of Herbs and Herbalism*. London: Orbis, 1979.

Thomson, William A R. *Healing Plants: A Modern Herbal*. McGraw-Hill, 1978.

Watt, J M and Breyer-Brandwyks, M G. *Medicinal and Poisonous Plants of Southern and Eastern Africa*. 2nd edition. London: E & S Livingstone Ltd, 1962.

INDEX

Illustrations indicated in **bold**, according to plate number.

206